HEROES and HISTORY

HEROES
and
HISTORY

ROSEMARY SUTCLIFF

Illustrations by Charles Keeping

LONDON: B. T. BATSFORD LTD
NEW YORK: G. P. PUTNAM'S SONS

First published 1965
Reprinted 1967

Made and printed in Great Britain
by Jarrold and Sons Ltd, London and Norwich
for the Publishers

B. T. BATSFORD LTD
4 Fitzhardinge Street, Portman Square, London, W.1

G. P. PUTNAM'S SONS
200 Madison Avenue, New York 16, N.Y

For Elizabeth Goudge
with my love

Contents

Preface

In this book I have gathered together for you the handful of Heroes who have their place in the history of Britain. No country has many, for the Hero is not a person one meets every day (life would be extremely uncomfortable if one did!), nor even every century. It is hard to know, still harder to tell, what makes the Hero, though when you find him, you know him instantly and beyond doubt. Being a great man, a great leader, someone supremely good and brave and wise, doesn't make a Hero; indeed, though he *may* be all these things, and is always a great man in one way or another, he very often is not particularly wise or good. But he has something about him that other men haven't got. He is, as it were, larger than life, and enlarges the lives of those who share his story. He has a special kind of magnetism that lives on after him, so that stories gather to him, even other men's stories, or tales that were old before he was born. He wears, like Cuchulain the Champion of Ulster, 'The Hero-light on his brow'; very often he dies young and violently, while still at the height of his powers; and the odd thing is that the real-life flesh and blood Hero does that quite as often as the legendary one that men have made up for themselves. But perhaps there was never a Hero, however magical and far removed from mortal man, who was not a real man at the very beginning, before the legends started.

Beowulf and Achilles, Robin Hood, Bayard and El Cid; Finn Mac Cumhal, Saladin, King Arthur, Romulus and William Wallace; they all have the indefinable 'larger-than-life' quality, whether they are characters of sober history or figures of legend and High Romance.

But this book is about Heroes and History, and so I have kept to those British Heroes who have a place in the history books, or at least some kind of historical basis under the legend and the romance. And I have dealt with them in their historical aspects, trying to find out the men behind the legends and fit them into their proper places in the story of Britain.

In reading the stories, you will notice that all but one of them belong to the ancient or Mediaeval world, which ended with the death of Richard III on Bosworth Field. The Modern world started next day with Henry VII (one of the few real breaks in history). And it is as though the thing that makes the Hero cannot thrive in the Modern world. We have had great men instead, some of them better and greater by far than some of the Heroes have been; but of them all, only one, James Graham, 1st Marquis of Montrose, wears the Hero-light on his forehead.

Oddly enough, I believe we may have produced another of the breed in this century. Lawrence of Arabia, a genius, a mystic, incredibly brave, intolerably cruel—to himself as well as others— a shameless exhibitionist, *but larger than life*. We are not far enough off from him yet, to be sure, but already legends have begun to gather, though they are legends of a different kind from those which surround Saladin and the Prince Llewellin.

Chapter 1

Caratacus

BRITAIN had three or four thousand years of history behind her when the Romans came, but we can only read it in the great stones that we call Stone Henge, in certain green trackways, in a smith's hoard of half-worked spear heads dredged from a river bed, a broken cooking pot with a chevron design on it turned up by a ploughshare, and in the green barrows along the downs, which, when opened, yield a pot of human ashes and a bronze dagger or a woman's skeleton and three beads of blue Egyptian glass, all that remains of a mighty warrior burned on a hero's pyre and laid away with his magic weapon, or a queen buried with her favourite necklace.

They must have had their Heroes, the dark people of the flint, the fair people of the bronze and gold, but their names are lost, and a Hero must have a name to be remembered by.

It is only with the first contact between Britain and Rome that the names of actual people begin to appear, and one of the first of these is Caswallon, King of the great Belgic Tribe whose capital stood where St Albans stands now. The Cattivlauni, they were called, 'The Cats of War', and the name was well earned, for by the time of Caswallon's grandson Cunobeline they had overrun most of the neighbouring tribes, or made vassals of them, so that they held a kind of shadowy sovereignty over most of Southern Britain. In A.D. 42, Cunobeline died, leaving his kingdom divided among his three sons. So the story begins like a folk tale: 'There was once a King who had three sons . . .' and in true folk-tale tradition, Caratacus was the youngest son.

Bericus, the eldest, proved such a bad king that the whole tribe, led by the two younger brothers rose against him. He escaped their spears and fled to Rome (Southern Britain had had dealings with Rome for a hundred years or more), taking with him the Sacred Crown and sword that made up the King's regalia.

Togodumnus, the second son, who was a brave man with a head too hot to have much sense in it, sent to the Emperor Claudius in the tone of equal sending to equal, to demand the return of both Bericus and the Crown Jewels, and the Emperor Claudius, who did not regard the lord of a few thousand fighting spears and a herd of white cattle as his equal, was annoyed at the tone of the demand and promptly refused it. Togodumnus replied smartly, by laying hold of all Roman-owned trading vessels which had the ill-luck to be in his ports, and sent again to Claudius to announce that he was holding them hostage until his demands were satisfied.

This, along with several other matters, such as the need to find an ultimate frontier for the Empire, made up the Emperor's mind for him. Ever since Julius Caesar's attempt almost a hundred years ago, it had been clear that Britain must come under the wingspread of the Roman eagle one day; and now the day had come.

In late summer of the next year, the Empire's greatest General, Aulus Plautius sailed from Gaul with an army of fifty thousand men, including the 2nd, 9th, 14th and 20th Legions. (The 2nd Augustan, which was to be the last to leave Britain nearly four hundred years later, was commanded by Vespasian who became Emperor himself, in his turn.) The plan had been to land on the nearest point of the British coast, but in the night a meteor shot across the sky travelling westward, and the Augurs who were with the army declared that this was an omen. And so the invasion fleet with its galley slaves straining at the oars and its generals pacing the deck, turned westward, each galley following the stern-brazier of the next ahead, and came to shore at last, far up the maze of lagoons and looping waterways which is now Chichester Harbour.

The British held the low shores and tidal mud flats against them so strongly that it was three days before they could gain a foothold. But they fought their way in from the shallows at last, and having driven back the defenders, raised a base camp of sorts and beached the galleys under its cover, and set out on the long inland march towards Lyndyn, which we call London.

Owing to various hitches on the other side of the Channel, it was well into August, and Togodumnus and his brother, who had waited under arms all summer long, had withdrawn their main War Host to Colchester, sure that the invasion would not come so late in the year; and many of the warriors had gone home to gather the harvest, when word of the landing reached them. They sent to the vassal kings in the south, to slow up the Roman advance as long as might be, and set to work to gather the army

14

again. The black goat was sacrificed, and the Cran-Tara was sent out, summoning the tribes, and from all across the south country, men took up their weapons and came in answer, leaving the women to finish the harvest.

And so when Aulus Plautius and his legions came over the scarp of the north downs, and dropped down towards the Thames, they found the royal brothers with their tributary princes and about sixty thousand men already waiting for them at the main ford. Earlier in the summer the Britons had cut channels across the ford itself, and built stockades along the northern bank, and now, from the cover of these, the warriors, stripped for battle and painted with blue war patterns after the British fashion, harassed the invaders with arrows and light throwing javelins as they struggled to make the ford passable again.

For three days, matters remained so, and then on the fourth night, when the waning moon was not yet up and the water under the trees was lost in blackness, three thousand Batavian auxiliaries, stripped naked, swam the river with their knives in their teeth. All Batavians, said the rest of the Empire, were born with webbed feet. The men about the British camp-fires heard no sound, not so much as the plop that a diving otter makes, until the Batavians were among them, hamstringing the chariot ponies or cutting free the picket ropes! Under cover of the turmoil, part of the 9th Legion got across by the half-mended ford, and the night went roaring up in battle.

Even then the British might have held, but their own war bands who had been posted upstream to guard against any crossing there, came rushing down to their comrades' aid; and so the 2nd Legion, led by Vespasian got ropes across at a point some miles further up, crossed over, and came charging down in their turn, shields linked, to take the British on the flank.

Long and valiantly the British held their ground, Caratacus alone their leader now for Togodumnus was dead with a Legionary spear in his throat. But in the darkness, taken by surprise and hampered by maimed and terrified ponies, their wild warrior-courage no match for the discipline of the Roman troops, they began at last to give way....

When dawn came, four thousand British lay dead, to nine hundred men of the Legions, and Caratacus had brought the remainder off, to fight another time—a more difficult thing for any leader than to lead them forward in victory.

He knew that the Romans' next thrust would be towards his capital at Colchester, and he pulled the British War Host back to a certain wooded ridge that curved across the track about a day's march north of Lyndyn; and here, joined by reinforcements from the midlands and the west country who had been too late for the river battle, he determined to make his stand. Indeed it was a place such as the Lady of Battles might have made for the purpose, with marshland to protect the left flank of the defenders, and on the right, the thick scrub clothing the ridge in such a fanged and interlaced tangle of thorn and bramble that no flanking force could possibly cut its way through; and on the forward slopes of the ridge below the woods, the ground was clear for chariots to manœuvre.

They had time to throw up stockaded camps at either end of the position and in the centre, and to cut clear-ways through the thorn woods for bringing up the reserves which could then be held out of sight until they were needed, for Aulius Plautius, realising the growing strength of the British, had made camp for himself and sent for reinforcements.

And then, early in September, the British scouts brought word to Caratacus that the Emperor Claudius had landed with an enormous force, and there were strange stories too of huge beasts among them, beasts as big and black as thunderclouds, with tails at both ends, at whose tread the hills shook, and whose voice was as the voice of a thousand warhorns.

Two nights later, the British on the ridge found themselves looking down at the camp-fires of the Legions all across the country south of them, until the September mist came up and blurred them out. Dawn came, and the whole horse-shoe curve of the ridge stood out darkly, the clear turf before it sloping down into the white sea of mist that hid the enemy from their strained and searching eyes. Caratacus, already standing in his chariot at the head of the right-wing column, while Catigern, his sister's husband, headed the left, sent out his scouts; and they returned quickly, with news that the Legions were advancing straight up the track towards the centre of the ridge. Maybe one of the scouts reported the sound of mallets echoing from the mist, but if so, Caratacus paid no heed, thinking it no more than tents or picket lines being shifted. Maybe the mist smothered the sound altogether. . . .

At last the tramp of feet and the jink of harness and the first faint shouted orders sounded in the mist, the Roman trumpets were suddenly sounding high and clear, and were answered by the wild hollow boom of the British warhorns; and away below, the vanguard of the 20th Legion rolled forward out of the mist, the first sunlight touching the spread, gilded wings of the eagle with fire.

Again the warhorns boomed, and the British Foot broke forward from the shadows of the thorn scrub and swept down to meet the shield-locked ranks of Rome. The battle centre was already joined, when Caratacus from the right flank and Catigern from the left, unleashed the chariot charge.

The British war-chariot, drawn by its team of fiery ponies, with its crew of driver and fighting man, its foot-warriors armed with long knives leaping along at each wheel—sometimes the wheels themselves armed with whirling sickle-blades—must always have been a horrifying sight to the men who saw it thundering towards them. And a King's chariot will have been fine and deadly above the common run. Caratacus at the head of his flying squadrons must have been a wonderful and fearful thing to see: Caratacus naked and patterned with the blue war-paint like his warriors, the gold collar of the Kingship round his neck, the early morning sun flashing back from the red enamel and gilded bronze of his buckler, the leaf-shaped blade of his spear, and the glittering harness-ornaments of the four-horse team, his fair hair flying back like the ponies' manes on the wind of his going. And behind him the whole chariot column; the screaming wheels and thunder of flying hooves, the high triumphant yell of the British war cry.

On and down they swept against the seemingly unprotected Roman flank. They began to meet the showers of lead from the Balearic slingers, but they were almost upon the enemy, swinging wide to fling in their charge against the rear flank which they had begun to see as the mist broke up. Then, seemingly for no reason, Caratacus' team stumbled and crashed headlong. The next chariot swept past, but crashed scarce a spear-throw ahead; then another, and another; those behind unable to swerve aside or pull up in time, crashed into them. The wreckage piled and spread, the chaos grew. The screams of the ponies mingled with the shouts of men and the splintering crash of chariots. Charioteers, the reins wrapped round their waists in the British fashion, to leave their hands free for fighting, were dragged helpless into the ghastly tangle and brained by the lashing hooves of their own teams. The trumpets sang again, and the Nubian spearmen swarmed forward to the kill.

Caratacus was flung clear when his chariot came down, and he struggled up and ran to the right, stumbling as he went over tent rope pegged knee-high in the long grass. The hammering in the mist and the disaster to the chariot charge were accounted for.

The last section of the column, the charioteers from the west country had had time to swerve clear and escape the havoc, and Caratacus sprang into the leading chariot which swerved aside to pick him up, and taking command, led the squadron back uphill towards the British reserves position. Then, ordering the real leader of the squadron to the aid of Catigern, who was fighting desperately on the left wing, outnumbered and partly surrounded, he put himself at the head of the remaining foot-warriors and led them downhill again in one last charge like a breaking wave on to the levelled spears and linked shields of the Legions.

It was all quite hopeless. With the chariot wings gone, the British were engulfed from either side by the Roman cavalry, and slowly crumpled up. The end came with a trembling of the ground and a crashing bellow as of a thousand warhorns, as the horrified warriors saw, surging down upon them, an ordered line of THINGS that were half animal, half walking fortress, so huge that their backs were in the sunlight while the last of the morning mist still wreathed about their legs!

The British War Host broke and streamed away, back towards the thorn woods and the clear-ways which now were their only way of escape.

Caratacus made one last desperate attempt to hold the river below Chelmsford, but the Legions and the pursuing elephants were upon them before the ford could be cut; and that was the end.

When dusk came, that hazy September day, close on five thousand British lay dead among hundreds of slaughtered chariot ponies and wrecked chariots, and eight thousand were captives in the enemy camp. Fugitives were scattered all across the country-side, and Caratacus, with the two hundred chariots still left to him, and his wife and young daughter, who like many of the British women, had rushed down to play their part in that last hopeless fight for the river ford, was thundering westward to throw in his lot with the Silures, the little dark tribesmen of south Wales.

The Emperor Claudius made a triumphal entry into Colchester, complete with elephants, and within a few days, having received the homage of various vassal kings, and declared Caratacus's Kingdom a Roman province with Aulus Plautius its first governor, departed back to Rome. There, he granted himself a Triumph, presented himself with a large number of decorations including the Legionary equivalent of the V.C. and called his newly born son Britanicus to commemorate the conquest of Britain.

But Britain was not yet conquered (a large part of the hill country never was) and nor was Caratacus.

The Roman Army was divided into four, and set about the task of bringing the whole island under the eagle. But the basic work was still not finished when, seven years and thirty pitched battles later, Aulus Plautius, by now a sick man, was recalled to Rome, and Ostorius Scapula sent out in his place.

Caratacus had not skulked in hiding, but had ridden the war trail all those seven years, at the head of the south Welsh tribes. The wild mountain country made a perfect base for raids and guerrilla warfare, and he had taken full advantage of it to make himself a thorn in the side of the Romans. But now, when Ostorius Scapula, having dealt with an uprising of the Brigantes in the north, turned his full force against him, he knew that the time of raids, of small garrisons cut off and marching columns ambushed, was over, and the long struggle was drawing to its end. Even so, it took the three Legions more than two years to subdue south and central Wales, and drive Caratacus up into the north. It was not only the man himself but the power he had to fire men's hearts with his own courage, so that his name ran like heath-fire through the hills and wherever he was, wherever men heard his name, they took heart and rallied. And he was as hard to stamp out as a heath-fire, too; yet the whole Roman Army knew that they must stamp him out, or never count their hold on Britain secure.

Several places in the border country of Wales claim the bitter honour of Caratacus's last stand, but the most likely is Caer Caradoc in Shropshire, where the green wave-lift ramparts of a great British camp still crown the hill. There, then, Caratacus stood to give battle for the last time, and there at last, the British War Host was defeated, taking with it a vast toll of Roman dead, but defeated, none the less. Caratacus's wife and daughter were captured, and he was faced with the hideous decision that other men have had to face in like circumstances, before and since. Which came first, his personal loves, or the thing he had fought for so long? He made his choice. He left them in Roman hands, and with a small band of his household warriors, headed northeast under cover of the dark.

A few days later he was at the gates of Aldborough, where Cartimandua, the Queen of the Brigantes, had her capital. It is easy enough to see in one's mind's eye, the huddled thatch of hall and houseplace, byre and barn, and the bothies that made up the

20

royal village. The chariot ponies grazing on the in-pasture, the heather washing to the very walls, the smoke of evening cooking fires hanging over all. And before the gates, in battered chariots harnessed to all but foundered ponies, a weary handful of men, most of them with some wound to show, who are all that is left of a great War Host.

They lay aside their weapons, and Caratacus with the rest behind him, is brought into Cartimandua's painted timber hall, where she sits in the high seat with Venutius the King beside her, waiting to receive him, for her look-outs have told her of his coming. She is much such a woman as Maeve of Connacht, strong and ruthless, her fair hair hanging straight on either side of her face under the enamelled crown. And her gown of dark plaid stuff is fastened at her shoulder with a brooch of red-gold as big as a man's fist. Caratacus stands before her, his few companions at his back, a tall man, golden-haired as she is herself, but there are grey streaks in his gold, and the lines on his face are deep cut as though with a sword, by the nine years' struggle that lies behind him. But he is not done with the struggle yet; he has come to her not for refuge, but because, remembering that only two years ago she also had Roman daggers at her heart, he hopes that she may help him now, to carry on the fight.

Cartimandua listens to him, but her mind is already made up. She is on good terms with the conquerors now and finds it very pleasant. She does not want trouble with the Red Crests again, and here is a chance to buy even more of their favour.

She makes a signal with her hand, and suddenly there are armed men in the doorway, armed men all round the hall, far outnumbering the little band. Caratacus's hand leaps to his sword, but the wolfskin sheath is empty, and the armed men close in. Perhaps Venutius half rises from his seat with some furious protest —he is no lover of Rome—but if so, Cartimandua scarcely even hears him. The Brigantes follow the Old Way, still; with them it is the women who rule, the Crown passing from mother to daughter. Cartimandua is the Queen in her own right, and Venutius is King only by right of his marriage to her. His eyes meet Caratacus's as the wrist and ankle chains are brought, and he cannot endure the look in them. He leaps up and rushes furiously from the hall.

Caratacus was sent to Rome in chains, like a violent slave.

The Emperor Claudius, delighted, decreed a public holiday, and the whole city turned out to watch him on his way through the streets. The Praetorian Guard was on parade, trumpets sounded, dogs barked, women held up their babies for a closer look, the sellers of cheap wine and sticky sweets did a roaring trade. And up the broad straight Flaminian Way towards the Forum area, under heavy guard as though even now they feared he might escape them, came the tragic small procession of British captives; and the holiday crowds fell oddly silent as they passed. First came the knot of household warriors who had stood with Caratacus in Cartimandua's hall, then a couple of waggons laden with his goods and gear, his armour and weapons and captured Roman gear recaptured at Caer Caradoc; his wife and daughter and kinsmen captured there also, and last of all, Caratacus himself, walking alone save for the guard a few paces behind him. Caratacus looking neither to right nor left, holding his head high, and carrying his captive's chains as though they had been the laurel garlands of a victor.

Claudius, seated on a raised tribunal platform in the Forum to receive his submission, was so impressed by his courage and noble bearing, that he gave orders that the chains were to be struck off, and the British King treated with all respect.

From that day he was allowed to live in honourable retirement —and in exile—in Rome, his kin and his household warriors with him. And so he passes out of all men's knowledge, though he may have lived on for many years. His story was over, and he must have known it to his heart's core. It is a sorry ending, the wrong ending for a Hero-tale. He should have died on the green ramparts of Caer Caradoc; maybe, sometimes, he wished he had.

Chapter 2

Arthur

MORE than four hundred years go by before another man steps out from the ruck of British history with the unmistakable Hero-light on his forehead. He is the greatest of the company, the one who has kept the strongest hold on our imagination through fifteen hundred years. He is King Arthur.

King Arthur. The name has gathered the sound of magic to it. Shut your eyes, and let the picture it conjures up grow behind them. It will be a picture with a background of silken pavilions, castles with bright heraldic pennants flying from their turrets, ladies in high-waisted gowns and head-dresses that are like folded gauze butterflies or tall and pointed like jewelled church-steeples, walking on turf as thick with flowers as the turf of the *Dame et la Licorne* tapestries. A world of high chivalry and magnificent adventures, washed in a golden light, but dark also with forests and strange shadows of fear under the trees. And the King Arthur who moves through this fifteenth-century background with his companions, with Guenivere his Queen, the touchy Sir Kay, the insufferably virtuous Galahad, Lancelot with his half dark nature, who tears at one's heart rather as St Peter does among the Disciples, is a knight in fifteenth-century armour.

He is the Hero of the book Sir Thomas Malory wrote in gaol and called *Le Morte d'Arthur*. Sir Thomas Malory, himself belonging to the time of The Wars of the Roses, set the whole story in a kind of magical version of the England he knew. It was a process that had been going on for a thousand years; everyone who retold the story putting it into his own day as though it was still happening.

Tennyson carried the process on. He did not put Sir Lancelot into a top hat nor Guenivere into a bustle, but none the less, in his *Idylls of the King* they are faintly Victorian, the ladies in particular reaching out towards the dying-duck, drop-wristed demoiselles of Burne-Jones's paintings.

Everyone knows the story of King Arthur and his knights of the

23

Round Table. If you have not read this same *Le Morte d'Arthur*
nor *Idylls of the King*, you must have read one or other of the
countless retellings, good, bad, or all too often, indifferent. But
here, in outline, it is again.

Once, in the ancient and chivalrous times, there was a King in
England called Utha Pendragon, who fell in love with a certain
Igraine who was wife to the Duke of Cornwall. Igraine, being as
virtuous as she was fair, did her best to hold him off, and told her
husband that they must leave the Court; and the Duke took her
back to Cornwall, to the great castle of Tintagel that clings like an
eagle's eyrie to the jagged cliffs above the Western Sea.

But Utha was a wild dark man not easily turned from his will,
and he followed hard after them, and summoned the Duke out
to meet him in battle. So there was bitter fighting between the
King and the Duke, each with their household knights, and in it
the Duke was slain. And that night, with the help of the magician
Merlin, Utha put on the likeness of the Duke of Cornwall, and
went into the castle as the master coming home weary from battle.
He went into the chamber of the Duchess Igraine and slept with
her under the sheepskins on the bedplace. And that night Arthur
was conceived.

Later, when Igraine knew that her Lord was dead, the King
came wooing her in his own likeness, and at last she yielded to
him and became his Queen. When Arthur was born, he was
smuggled away by Merlin (as some say because the King had
enemies who might have sought his life, or as others say, simply
because he was born before he should have been) who gave him
to an old knight called Sir Ector, to bring up as his own son.

So Arthur was bred up with Kay, Sir Ector's son, and trained
in all arts of war and courtesy that became a knight, until the time
that he was fifteen years old. Then King Utha Pendragon died,
as some said of poison; and all through the Kingdom there was
uproar and uncertainty, for he had, so men thought, left no son
to come after him.

Then Merlin went to the Archbishop and bade him call together
all the nobles and knights of the land for a great jousting at
Christmastime, for Christ would make some miracle while they
were gathered together, to show who among them should be their
rightful king.

So the Archbishop called together all the knights and nobles
of the Kingdom, and among them old Sir Ector, with his son Kay
who had just been dubbed knight, and young Arthur to act as his
squire. All London was crowded and coloured and noisy as a

24

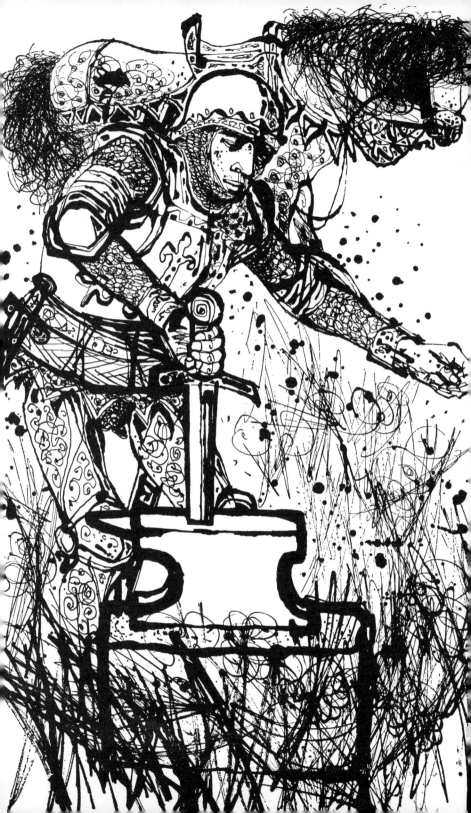

fairground. They found lodging in an inn for the night, and next morning set off with the great stream of knights and ladies and humble folk all going the same way, towards the tilting ground. But with the excitement of the crowds and the city and the prospect of tilting among grown and famous knights for such a prize, Kay forgot his sword, and did not discover its lack until they were almost at the field. Then he flew into a great state, blamed Arthur for not having carried out properly his duties as a squire, and bade him ride back full speed to fetch it from their lodging.

Arthur wheeled his horse and set off back the way they had come. But now he was going against the stream and could make but slow progress. It was some way back to their inn, and already he thought he heard the trumpets blowing from the lists; and he was afraid that he would not be able to get back with the sword before it was Kay's turn to joust. Now his road lay past a church, and in the churchyard, as he forced his way along, he saw the most beautiful and potent sword that he had ever seen, standing upright in a great anvil, which stood in its turn on a block of stone. He had not heard the story of this marvel that had appeared and he did not stop to wonder what the sword was doing there, and never even noticed that there was any writing on the hilt. 'Whoso pulleth out this sword of this stone and anvil is rightwise King born of all England.' He saw only that it was a sword, and because Kay needed it, he dismounted and drew it from the anvil and the stone, then mounting into the saddle again, went clattering back to where the other two would be waiting for him.

'This is not my sword', Kay said, when Arthur gave it to him. And Arthur told how he had found it and drawn it from the stone. Then Kay would have pretended that it was he who had drawn the sword. But old Sir Ector saw the writing on the hilt and knew at last who his foster son was, and knelt to him as the new King.

The Knights of the King's Council were not so easily convinced, especially as there were some among them who had hoped to be King themselves; and they made Arthur replace the sword in the anvil and each of them tried in turn to pull it out again. When all had failed—for indeed the blade seemed fused with iron and stone, Arthur drew it out again as easily as from a well-oiled sheath.

Then all men knew he was indeed the heir of Utha Pendragon, the new King. And he was crowned with great ceremony, and all his father's lords swore fealty to him.

Now Igraine his mother had borne three daughters to the Duke of Cornwall before ever the King cast his eye upon her, and one of these half-sisters about whom he knew nothing, was Maugose, Queen to King Lott of Orkney, and had four sons of her own (all of whom later became Arthur's knights). And when Arthur was crowned, she came to Court. She was very beautiful, though so much older than her half-brother, and they do say that all three sisters were witches and that she cast her spells upon the young King for the sake of gaining power. But however that may be, she slept with him one night, as his father had slept with the Duchess Igraine, and far away, back in Orkney, nine months later, Mordred was born.

Some tidied-up versions pretend that Mordred was King Lott's son, and only nephew to King Arthur, but that destroys the whole point of the story. For if Arthur did not commit the sin of begetting Mordred on his half-sister, the tragic and inevitable pattern of cause and effect, whereby Mordred is in the end the death of Arthur and the ruin of all that he had worked and fought for ceases to have any meaning. The claim that for full- or even half-brother and sister to mate and have young is 'against nature' is not really true; all animals do it quite naturally. In ancient Egypt it was the usual custom for Pharaoh to marry his sister so that the royal line should continue pure. But if it was done through too many generations, or if there was any sickness in the family, the stock became weakened; and men must have had some idea of this very early, for among most peoples, even from the time when men lived in caves, it has been looked on as a deadly sin.

Arthur, horrified to find that he had done this terrible thing, tried to wipe out one sin with another, and had the babe set adrift in a leaky boat. But Fate is not so easily turned aside. The babe was rescued, and reared, and grew to be a man. . . .

Meanwhile Arthur came by his own sword, his great sword Excalibur, given to him by the Lady of the Lake. And he married Guenivere, the daughter of a lesser king, who brought with her the Round Table for a dowry; and he gathered a great company of knights who flocked to him from all parts of Britain and even from overseas, and with them fought twelve great battles against the Saxons or the Irish. They became the hope of the weak and the terror of evildoers, the champions of right against wrong. They were to Britain what Charlemagne's Paladins were to France, and like Charlemagne's Paladins, each had their own adventures, strung on the thread of the main story. Sir Gawaine and the Loathley Lady, Gareth and Lynette, Garaint and Enid,

King Pelinore and the Questing Beast; Lancelot and Elaine—Lancelot who was his dearest friend and betrayed him by becoming Guenivere's lover. So the stories run on, linking and interlinking, until at last the time came when the Company of the Round Table broke up and set out, each man alone with his own soul, on the shining and tragic quest of the Holy Grail, from which so few of them returned.

Mordred, when he was grown to be a man, came to his father's Court, filled with dark and ancient hatreds that his mother had bred in him. Soon he had gathered a following of his own among the younger knights, and the shadows began to draw in. . . .

Lancelot was among the few who returned from the Grail quest, and the King was joyful to see him once again. But his love was still towards Guenivere and hers towards him, and Arthur turned his eyes away and pretended to know nothing, because he loved them both so well that anything seemed better to him than that harm should come to them. It was Mordred who betrayed them, all three, warning the King of how it was with the other two, before the whole Court, so that he could no longer pretend he did not know that they were lovers. And Arthur must act as befitted a King. Sir Lancelot he sent into exile, but Guenivere must fall to the Law, as a Queen who had betrayed her Lord, and she was tried and condemned to be burned at the stake; and he must leave her to her fate, because always he had told people 'It is for the Law to decide. The Law must punish or not punish as the judgment goes.'

But Sir Lancelot, hearing in his exile, what was to be the Queen's fate, came back to her rescue, and in the very last moment before the torch was set to the faggots, charged his horse through the crowd and the guards about her, and snatched her from the edge of death and bore her away with him.

He carried her to the coast, and overseas to his own castle of Joyous Guarde. Arthur followed to lay siege to the castle, and while he camped before it with all his chivalry, word was brought to him that Mordred had raised the standard of revolt, joined his forces with King Anguish of Ireland and other old enemies, and proclaimed himself King, declaring that his father was dead.

Then Arthur raised the siege, and took ship once more for England, and drove Mordred and his followers westward like an avenging storm. But Mordred had grown strong, and his allies were many, for there were tyrants in plenty who hated Arthur for putting down of tyranny. And many of the common folk, hearing that their King was dead, had lost heart, and now did not believe that he still lived after all. And in the west of the land, Mordred turned like a boar at bay, and there was a great battle, and Arthur's trumpets sounded for the last time. And when it was over, the flower of Arthur's knights lay dead with the piled dead of Mordred's following. And Arthur had slain his son, and Mordred with his dying stroke had wounded his father to the death, though the life yet lingered in him like the last blue spark in a sinking lamp.

Then the few of Arthur's knights who were yet left, lifted him and bore him to a hermit's cottage among the reedy marshes and when Sir Bedivere, who had been close to him almost all his life, had taken the great sword Excalibur at the King's bidding, and thrown it into the lake that lapped close by, and seen it taken back by the white arm of the Lady who had given it to him when he was young, there came a boat moving of itself, over the water, with three queens in it. And the King bade Sir Bedivere lift him into the boat, saying that he was going to Avalon the Island of Apples, which is also the place of the dead, to be healed of his grievous wounds. The queens received him, weeping, and the fairest of them took his head into her lap, and the boat drifted out again into the reeds and the mist, and Sir Bedivere, left lonely, stood on the bank to watch it go.

And never again was King Arthur seen by men, though Sir Lancelot, following after and seeking everywhere for his lord, heard a strange tale from a hermit, of a dead man who had been brought to him by three dark queens, and whom he had buried among the hills inland. But no man ever saw that grave, nor knew if it was indeed Arthur's.

Then Sir Lancelot stripped off his armour and threw away his sword, and turned himself wholly to God. And only once in the rest of his life, he left the little hermitage among the reed beds and the winding waterways, and that was to go to look one last time upon his love Guenivere, when she lay dead in the nunnery where she too had turned herself to God.

So—there it is in briefest outline. And the strange thing is that during the centuries that the legend grew in richness and wonder, Arthur himself somehow got submerged in it. Save for his beginning and ending, he is really little more than the bright thread on which the stories of his knights are strung; and it is Sir Lancelot who steps forward into the chief place. Malory himself seems to feel this, for at the very last, the wonderful lament that ends *Le Morte d'Arthur* is spoken by Sir Ector de Maris not for Arthur at all, but for Sir Lancelot, lying dead in his hermit's rough brown habit.

Thou, Sir Lancelot, there thou liest, that thou were never matched of earthly knight's hand. And thou were the courtliest knight that ever bear shield. And thou were the truest friend to thy lover that ever bestrad horse. And thou were the truest lover of a sinful man that ever loved woman. And thou were the kindest man that ever struck with sword. And thou were the goodliest person that ever came among press of knights. And thou was the meekest man and the gentlest that ever ate in hall among ladies. And thou were the sternest knight to thy mortal foe that ever put spear in rest.

Arthur has got lost in another way, too. He is a Hero whose legend has grown into a vast shining haze, so intricate and many layered and many branched about him that for centuries it ceased to be believed that there was any real man behind the legend at all; and only in the past few decades have archaeologists, historians and anthropologists come to believe again that there was.

Now, come back close on a thousand years beyond Malory's England, fifteenth-century 'Romance England'. The last Legions have left Britain and we are on the edge of the dark, the last lights of the Christian faith and all civilisation going out around us. And out of this storm-murk rises the figure of a man, a great man who has not had time yet to become a legend. His formal Roman name is Artorius, but his fellow-countrymen for the most part call him Artos, which in the old British tongue means a bear.

It might even be possible to make a guess at the family he comes from. Magnus Maximus, the sword-made Emperor who comes so strongly to life in Rudyard Kipling's stories of the Roman Wall, is also the hero of an ancient Welsh legend in which he marries a British Princess, and certainly, if he did so, it would enormously strengthen his claim to the Purple, among his own legions, who by this time were mostly British born and bred wherever their great grandfathers came from. When, almost a hundred years later, Ambrosius Aurelianus appears as a British leader against the Saxons, his ancestry is traced from Maximus, and the Monkish chronicler Gildas says that his forefathers had 'worn the Purple' which suggests that he did belong to a British Royal House as strongly rooted in the Roman world as in the Celtic. And it has been a tradition from very early times that Arthur was a kinsman of Ambrosius, also that there was something mysterious about his birth. Therefore, it is not stretching possibility too far to think that he may have been one of that old Royal House. He is not mentioned in the Welsh genealogies; very well then, a bastard member. That would also explain why he is never once called 'King' in the early sources, though oddly enough he is twice given the title of Emperor.

His usual title in those early sources, is Comes Britanniorum, Count of Britain. Now in late Roman times, the Comes Britanniorum was the commander of a mobile force for the defence of all and any part of Britain that happened to be threatened. If Arthur was appointed, or appointed himself Count of Britain it would explain how he came to be remembered as a national and not merely a local leader, at a time when Britain had fallen back into its old separate princedoms and had no longer any kind of unity. The other interesting thing about the Count of Britain is that he was first and foremost a cavalry commander—a very possible beginning for the legend of a King and his band of knights.

Most of the very earliest references to Arthur are to be found in the writings of Welsh monks and churchmen, and they are generally rude. There are accounts of how he stole the pigs of one holy man, demanded another's shirt off his back and was immediately sunk into the ground up to his chin by Divine wrath. They show him, in fact, as a marauder. And the explanation may very well be that he requisitioned Church property to supply his army. Charles Martell, two hundred years later, struggling to hold the Moors back from Christian France thought the same way. 'If I keep the thatch on the byre it is but fair if I have a share of the corn out of it to feed my men.' But the Church did not see it that way.

So, the picture of a real man begins to emerge. But as the years after his death went by, strange twilight Celtic imaginings began to gather round the memories of the man. Hills, cromlechs, hill forts that were ancient before the Romans came, became Arthur's Hill, Arthur's Kitchen, Arthur's Seat, Arthur's Stone, Arthur's Hall. In a cave near Melrose Abbey, he lies in an enchanted slumber; in another near Snowdon his knights are sleeping until he calls them; near Carnarvon, occasional wanderers have seen his treasure. At Llyn Berfog in Merioneth his horse made a hoof-mark in the rock; in Builth in Brecknockshire his hound Cabal made a footprint in a great stone, and however far the stone is carried away one night it is always in its place again next morning. Stories belonging to other men, even stories belonging to the gods, some of them far older than Roman Britain were added, layer upon layer. Even the Grail Quest is one of these; the British had legends of quests for magic cups and cauldrons of Life, long before Christ was crucified, and so Arthur became the hero of a quest for the great Cauldron of Annwn which is watched over by nine maidens in the Land of Youth. The story turned Christian by and by, and so became the Quest of the Holy Grail.

But all this was Celtic and wolf-wild, no nearer than the Count of Britain, to Malory's fifteenth-century Arthur. Arthurian romance as we know it, took shape under the patronage of Henry II's Queen Eleanor, and it was the elaborate chivalry of her day, and the troubadour's idea of courtly love, that gave it the shape it has carried ever since. It was, for instance, about that time, from Henry's Breton domains, that Sir Lancelot first appears.

And so the thing comes to its full and curious and beautiful flowering at last with Sir Thomas Malory's *Le Morte d'Arthur*. But away behind it, almost a thousand years behind, we can still catch here and there, a faint glimpse of Artorius, Artos the Bear.

To reconstruct his story from the clues that still survive in the ancient chronicles, in known history and Welsh Bardic tradition, and the leas lying at the bottom of legends and folk tales, is rather like a cross between following a complicated detective problem and trying to work a jigsaw puzzle with half the pieces missing. But the result might be something like this:

He was a member, probably bastard, of the old Royal House of Britain, born in the second half of the fifth century, when the Romans had already left Britain to protect herself as best she could from the in-swarming Saxons. He came from somewhere in the west, from the hill country, not the lowlands, and got his first training as a fighter in the raiding and cattle rieving to which the tribes had returned after their years of Roman rule. After a while he joined forces, somewhat loosely, with his kinsman Ambrosius, who now ruled most of Southern Britain, and while the older man continued to hold this heart-land of Britain against the Saxon invader, he gathered his band of cavalry, taking the old title of Comes Britanniorum which would give him some kind of standing with the different Kings and Princes. At first he merely threw in his cavalry wherever it was needed by any ruler hard pressed; but little by little he gained influence until he became virtually War Leader of the whole of Britain.

Ambrosius abdicated or died or in some other way faded from the story. And Arthur was left alone, with the whole defence of Britain in his hands. But he had strong hands, and in twelve great battles he thrust the Saxons back. Nennius, writing in the eighth century gives the names of these battles, and they show that his first serious campaign was against the Anglo-Saxons who had forced their way in through the Wash and the Humber. For this campaign he made his base at Lincoln, and using the Roman roads that radiated from the city like the spokes of a chariot-wheel, thrust back both groups. Then he moved north and west, fighting a sharp engagement with the Saxons south of York; another close before Chester 'The City of Legions'. From there he moved beyond the Wall to suppress an uprising of British chieftains in league with the Picts, then turned south again to campaign in Norfolk and Suffolk.

All this took upward of twenty years. He was little more than a boy at the beginning, a middle-aged man when the whole Bar-barian horde, combining for the first time, with Aelle, King of the South Saxons for their chosen War Leader, set about one supreme effort to crush him. The result was the last great battle of the twelve, Badon, fought in all likelihood on and around Liddington Hill, just across the White Horse Vale from Swindon. The larks still sing over Liddington as they did in Arthur's day, and the wild blue cranesbill flowers along the foot of the ancient earthworks; there is nothing to tell one that here, the British broke the Saxon's power, and drove them back to the very fringes of the coasts where first they had landed; nothing to tell of the hoof-thunder of Arthur's cavalry on the turf as they swept down in the final charge that broke the Saxon shield-wall and won for Britain twenty years of respite from the Barbarians and the dark.

It may be that after the Badon fight, with the victory running hot like fire-drink in their veins, the British soldiers set Arthur up in their midst and shouted for him by the old half-forgotten name of Caesar. Maybe there was some ceremony, with much shouting, and he was proclaimed Emperor as Magnus Maximus had been. If so, no other part of the dead Western half-Empire or the still-living Eastern half ever heard of it—why should they, after all? Britain was by then no more than an island cut off from the rest of the world and lost in the northern mists. But it would explain the twice that he is spoken of as Imperator.

For twenty years he held his shield over Britain, and then. . . . We shall never know what happened, but the Welsh bards sing of Mordred as his father's enemy, far back in the early days. Maybe the story ended much as it does in *Le Morte d'Arthur* with that last dim battle in the west.

One thing, out of all this mass of likelihood and possibility, we know; and it is that if Arthur, if some man with the Hero's quality of being larger than life, had not risen to thrust back the Barbarians midway in their two-hundred-year-long invasion, the Saxon conquest would have come more quickly and in a different way. The British and their last heritage of Roman civilisation would have been engulfed, instead of having time to blend with and in some ways leaven the conquerors. It is because this man won the great battle of Badon that the light never quite went out in the Western hills, and even in Lowland Britain not until the battle of Dyram, only fourteen years before St Augustine kindled it again.

Chapter 3

Alfred

THE Saxons have settled, and Britain east of the Welsh Marshes and south of Hadrian's Wall has become England, and new marauders threaten the coastline; new sea-wolves, savage as the Saxons of Arthur's day. It is more than three hundred years since Arthur fell at Camlan, and the Saxons have changed; and a new Hero stands astride a menaced kingdom. It is Alfred of the White Horse Vale, and with him we come back out of the mists, to solid history.

In the year 849, in the Royal Manor at Wantage, a fifth son was born to Ethelwulf of Wessex and his Queen Osburg, and they called him Alfred. From the first, from long before he could put a meaning to the words, he must have heard all round him, talk of the Viking raids, the yellow-haired devils in the dragon-prowed fleets that swept down from the captured Shetlands to overrun the Orkneys and the Western Isles, ransacked the holy places of Iona and Clonmacnois, even plundered St Patrick's own cathedral at Armagh; the sea-wolves who, summer after summer, set the smoke of burning farmsteads rolling across the coastwise shires from Devon round to Northumberland.

Maybe he was scuffling with the puppies round the fire in the smoky hall (he was only two years old) when news came that his half-brother Athelstan had won a great victory over the Danish fleet off Sandwich, and heard the rejoicing and gathered that the tree-tall half-brother he saw so seldom had done something wonderful, though he could not quite understand what. But under the fierce flare of rejoicing at the news, there was still anxiety, for London had gone up in flames, and the Danes in Mercia had finally flung back the defeated King and were across the Thames into Wessex. Ethelwulf and his second son Ethelbald had called out the Fyrd (the Militia) and marched to meet them, and it might be that even at this moment the two War Hosts were locked in battle.

A few days later another messenger, on an almost foundering

35

horse, came drumming up to the Manor House in the green Berkshire Downs, with word that the King and his son had gained a mighty victory.

But even then, some grey-muzzled warrior too old to carry his sword in the War Host shook his head and muttered that no victory could undo the fact that with their winter camp on the Isle of Thanet, the Vikings had spent all last winter on English soil, as they had never done before. And someone told him not to croak like a bird of ill omen; but those who heard him glanced at each other knowing in their hearts that he was right, that the Viking menace had passed the stage of raids and reached the stage of settlement. It was no passing thing and no single victory could end it.

When Alfred was four, the new young King of Mercia called on Ethelwulf for aid against the Welsh, who were harrying the western counties. All this fighting must have come hard on Ethelwulf, for he was not a soldier by nature like his mighty old father who had freed Wessex from the power of Mercia and made her great. He was a scholar and a religious man who would have been happiest in the quiet of a monastery. None the less, he rallied to the call for aid, and again gathered the Fyrd, and dealt with Wales with a strong hand. And the following Easter, all old quarrels between the two kingdoms were finally healed by the marriage of his little daughter Ethelswith to the King.

Maybe as she was so young—she was next to Alfred in the family, not more than six or seven years old—they may not have taken her away from her family for a few more years, but in any case, Alfred had little time to miss her just then; for before him, that summer, lay a tremendous adventure! For years his father had longed to go on a pilgrimage to Rome, and now, despairing of being able to set out for several years more, he determined to send his youngest son instead. Why the youngest, no one can say, but maybe Ethelwulf had some foreboding that none of his three tall elder sons, but this, the rather delicate baby, was the one who would bear the burden of Kingship after him; or again, with all France in flames, and the Vikings well across the way so that the journey must be a hideous risk, the youngest and best beloved was the one who could be best spared.

The little party set off, and despite all dangers, arrived safely. Pope Leo IV received the little boy as his 'Spiritual Son' and 'Girded him with the honour and the outward array of Nobility after the manner of the Consols at Rome'.

Poor little boy!

That winter his mother died and next year he was on the road to Rome again, with his father who had decided that he must, after all, make the pilgrimage himself. They remained nearly a year in Rome, Ethelwulf seeking council of the new Pope, Benedict III, visiting many shrines and offering wonderful gifts of Saxon goldsmiths' work to St Peter's Church; a cross, two basins, two statues, all of purest gold, a gold-bound sword, hanging silvergilt supports for sanctuary lights, silken vestments gleaming with embroidery in jewels and golden thread.

On the way home at last, they spent several weeks with Charles the Bald of France, while treaties were discussed and made and signed, binding the two Kings as allies against the Viking terror. And the last link of this bond was forged by a marriage between Ethelwulf and the French Princess Judith. The wedding and the new Queen's crowning were celebrated at the royal castle of Verberie-sur-Oise, when the great forest of Compiègne was blazing golden with October, and one wonders what Alfred, six years old and with his own mother not much more than a year dead, felt as he watched this thirteen-year-old stepmother move through her wedding and coronation; heard the voice of the Archbishop of Rheims:

The Lord crown thee with Glory and Honour and place upon thy head the precious stones of the Spirit; that whatsoever is here of token in the sheen of gold and the varied sparkling of jewels, may ever shine forth in thee and in thy doings: which thing may He Himself vouchsafe to grant, to Whom is honour and glory for all ages to come.

Whatever Alfred thought, however good the marriage was for binding France and England together, it caused trouble in Wessex from the start. During the King's absence Athelstan the eldest prince had died, and the rule had been taken over by Ethelbald, the second. Now, angry at his father's long absence and enraged by the sudden appearance of a strange Queen in his mother's place, Ethelbald rose against his father with a large following behind him. And to save Wessex from the horrors of civil war, Ethelwulf yielded up the main Kingdom, and retired to the smaller territory of Kent, Sussex and Surrey which until now had been the elder son's portion. In two years he was lying in his tomb at Winchester, and the territory he had held had passed to Ethelbert, the third brother. Two more years, and Ethelbald also was dead, and Ethelbert had combined the whole Kingdom into one, and kept it so for the five years of his rule.

All those years the long bitter struggle with the Northmen went on, but save for the black times, such as the attack on Winchester, it remained in the background of life for young Alfred. The Royal Manors at Wantage, Winchester and Chippenham were all home to him, and from Wantage, where he had been born and lived those first small contented years with his mother, he must often have ridden along the skirts of the White Horse Vale, past the great time-blurred turf ramparts of the hill fort where more than three hundred years before, Arthur had fought his great battle against the Saxon-kind. Maybe if the day was hot and the swallows flying high, he would turn his horse loose to graze, and lie down in the curve of the vast rampart, where the wild blue cranesbill was in flower, and listen to the larks overhead as Arthur must have done.

He had a good life, though a hard one; he hunted deer and wild boar with the King and nobles; and with the other boys of the King's following, ran and swam and wrestled, and learned the use of sword, spear and buckler, and the short Saxon bow. And in the evenings he listened to the tales of passing travellers, and the songs and hero-sagas of the minstrels, that he loved. Although he came later to be a fine scholar, he was not a great one for his lessons in those days, and one can even imagine, somewhere in the background, a harassed tutor tearing his hair. For despite the charming story of how Alfred won the beautiful illuminated book that his mother had promised to whichever of the children should learn to read first, Alfred himself said when he was a grown man, that he had not learned to read until he was twelve years old, and that he bitterly regretted it.

Yet whatever he was like at his formal studies, from the first he was one of those who draw their education from every contact with life; everything he saw, he saw with his whole heart, and to everything he brought an enormous exploring interest. He watched the serfs ploughing and reaping, the huntsmen with the hounds, the grooms in the stables, the girls in the women's quarters at their spinning and weaving, the wainwrights and the blacksmiths at their tasks, and asked the reason for this and that, and remembered afterwards. He talked with the stewards and bailiffs, he asked the monks working in the monastery herb-plots which herbs were for flavouring venison and which for an aching tooth or a green wound.

The meaning of his Christian Faith he learned with the same whole heart, for in his feeling for the things of God he was very much his father's son.

38

And then Ethelbert died and was laid beside his elder brother at Sherborne, and Ethelred, only a few years older than Alfred, came to the throne. And as though the change of King had been a signal, the comparative quiet of the past five years went roaring up in fire and tempest.

And Alfred, at sixteen, was suddenly a man and called on to do the work of a man and the King's brother. Through all that followed, he went shoulder to shoulder with the King of Wessex, his second in command both at the council fire and in the battle line. He was a born soldier, like Richard III who was also in command of an army when he was sixteen, and not because he was the King's brother.

He needed all his powers as a soldier in the years that followed, and something more than a soldier's courage, for he had battles of his own to fight as well as battles with the Danes. Alfred has been described as a bright flame burning in a frail lamp, and the description is a just one. For although he was no weakling he was certainly not strong; almost from his boyhood he had some kind of stomach trouble, gallstones very likely, so that off and on throughout his life, he had to carry pain with him. Also he had what was called in those days 'The Falling Sickness' and we call epilepsy. It is a strange thing that 'The Falling Sickness' seems to have some link with the qualities that make a great soldier or a leader of men. Saul, Alexander the Great and Paul of Tarsus were all epileptics, and in early times the sickness was looked on as a mark of Divine favour; but it cannot have made life easier for a young man who, under the King, led the armies of Wessex in time of desperate and worsening danger!

The danger swept in like great storm waves pounding further and further up a beach. The Northmen and Danes had had their fill of scattered raiding; the first sign of it had come in that summer when Alfred was two years old; now the time had come for conquest and settlement, and from all points the Vikings descended, like a bee swarm that has left the old hive, even the women and children, their dogs and falcons with them. In the autumn of 865 two brothers, Halfdan and Ivar the Boneless landed with a huge Danish War Host. They poured over East Anglia, and spent the winter there, gathering arms and horses in huge numbers. The following autumn they seized and occupied York, and held the place till spring, when the men of Northumbria rallied to drive them out. The battle cost both Saxon and Viking heavy in dead and wounded, and when the day ended, the Danes were still in York. There they remained through the summer, harrying the country around. And then in October they spilled out, southward into Mercia, where they made their winter camp at Nottingham.

Again the King of Mercia appealed to Wessex for aid, and in the spring the two brothers marched north with the Wessex War Host. But for Alfred that summer contained another thing than fighting—indeed there was little fighting, for the Danes behind the strong Roman walls of Nottingham refused battle, and there was nothing for the Mercian King to do but make peace—for some time before he marched south again with Ethelred, he married Aellswith the daughter of a Mercian Nobleman.

That autumn the Vikings broke up and returned to York, which they held for another year, before heading back for East Anglia again, to make their winter camp at Thetford on the Norfolk-Suffolk border. For a year they lived on the farms and harvests of East Anglia, and on the very edge of winter, marched for Wessex itself.

By that time Ivar was gone to rule the Viking Settlement in Ireland, and the Danish War Host that swarmed into Berkshire followed the raven standard of Halfdan alone. They pitched camp not far from the Royal Manor of Reading, and spent three days building a strong stockade round it; and then sat themselves down as usual in winter quarters, and also as usual smoke rose from burning farmhouses and the cattle were driven off for slaughter and the women carried away for slaves.

Through the icy wind of January, King Ethelred and his young brother brought the men of Wessex up at forced march. At dusk they attacked the stockade, the Danes swarmed out to meet them, swinging the great Viking axes that were their most hideous weapon. All across the rough ground below the camp the fight raged, far into the bitter dark of the winter night, but in the end, it was the Saxons who broke and gave back and once again the Danes were left in possession.

Ethelred and Alfred withdrew on Reading, set grimly to work to get the War Host once more into battle trim and put fresh heart into them, and within four days, the armies faced each other again, somewhere high on the Downs, above the White Horse Vale. Maybe from where they stood under arms, Alfred could see the green ramparts crowning Badon Hill, and if he turned about, catch a foreshortened view of the strange bird-headed horse cut half-hillside high in the chalk across the Vale. And here, where British and Saxon had met in desperate battle, now, Saxon stood to meet Dane.

It was still early, with the red and gold of a stormy winter dawn flaming across the sky, but the Danish warhorns were already snorting for battle. Alfred, in command of the Saxon's left wing, waited for the answering horn-challenge from the right wing where his brother commanded, that would be the order to set-on; but it did not come. He sent urgently for orders, and his messenger came panting back with word that Ethelred was still in his tent, for it was the hour of Mass. Alfred sent again, to bid him to leave the Mass, for the enemy were showing signs of movement. But Ethelred the King, fully armed yet still kneeling before the priest in his tent, sent back a sharp answer. He was at Mass, and would not leave the service of God for the service of Man. . . .

Alfred hung on a while longer. He could sympathise with Ethelred, for he too was very much his father's son, but surely God could not feel that one Mass left unfinished mattered more than a whole Christian War Host defeated by the Heathens! All along the dark Danish lines under the spread-winged Raven Banners, he saw the ripple of movement that at any moment might become a surge forward. What in God's sweet name must he do? He was only the second in command. . . . But suddenly he knew that there was only one thing to do, and if he was wrong— but there was no time to think of that. He raised his own great horn of Narwhal ivory to his lips, and sent the Saxon war-note booming across the cold morning air. There was a moment's tingling silence, and then from the right wing the call was taken up and came back to him like an echo. And even as the Danish battle line began to move, under the braying of their own war-horns, the Host of Wessex raised the war cry and rolled forward to meet them.

The shields crashed together, and as the surf of battle-shouting rose into the wintry air, Ethelred came running from his tent, the Mass over, his drawn sword in his hand.

On the crest of the High Downs, a lone ancient thorn tree reached gaunt arms to the sky, and all about it the battle raged, over the hound-tawny turf made treacherous by the winter wet, still more treacherous as time went by, with the slipperiness of blood. It was dusk, the early winter dusk, before the Northmen began, slowly at first and then more swiftly, to give ground. . . .

They left five earls behind them among their dead; they stumbled away into the darkness with the Wessex men yelling on their heels. At dawn, those that were left of them stumbled back into their camp by Reading. And the Saxons stood leaning on their spears, and knew that at last they had won a victory.

But within a fortnight the Danes were out from their camp, leaving it only lightly defended behind them, and were away under cover of a blinding snowstorm. Once more the wolf-pack was loose in Wessex and by the time the Wessex men caught up with them again, they had joined with others of their kind, and were entrenched in a new strongpoint a few miles from Basingstoke, on firm ground surrounded by marshes.

Ethelred launched an attack from the marshes, only to be driven back. And two months passed in raids and small forays before, in mid-Lent, the two armies again faced each other in full battle array. At first the Wessex men seemed to be going to repeat their victory above the White Horse Vale, but at the instant of finally sweeping forward to drive the Raven Banners from the field, the shout went up that Ethelred the King was fallen— wounded or dead, no one knew which—and dismay seized upon his soldiers, and in the instant of their wavering, the Northmen rallied and crashed forward again; and the day that had so nearly been a Saxon victory ended in defeat and bitter loss.

Ethelred was not dead, but so sorely wounded that though he lingered at Wimborne until Eastertime, all men knew that there was no hope for his life, and his last days must have been made darker by the knowledge that another Danish War Host had landed to the aid of their comrades in the coming summer, and joined the Northmen's camp at Reading.

On April 23rd the messengers set out, riding far and wide through the towns and villages of Wessex, with the word that the King was dead. And Alfred, standing with those of the household warriors who kept the death-vigil round the King's body, must have felt his heart near to breaking, not only for the loss of the brother he loved, but with the knowledge that now he was alone, that without any brother's counsel he must step forward to lead his people against the terrible redoubled host of the Northmen.

He buried his brother in Wimborne Minster and set the past behind him. There was no time for grieving nor for doubts. It had been hard enough while he shared his brother's burden; now he must bear it alone. . . .

In the next year he fought nine battles against the Danes, with raids and skirmishes beyond counting. From end to end of Wessex the young King rode with his army, and the army gave him of their best, loving him as they had never loved even his brother. But love and loyalty were not enough; all through that year the War Host was growing weaker. Their farms had been burned, their cattle and even their women driven off. They were weary and sick and growing more so. And at the year's end, seeing the wounds and the famished faces, Alfred did what was perhaps the hardest thing he ever had to do. He called together his Councillors, and with their agreement offered peace to the invaders— peace, and gold, the Dane geld, if they would leave Wessex also in peace.

The Northmen agreed; they had had a mauling, and perhaps they too needed a breathing space, and for four years the Wessex men were able to plough and harvest their fields as they had done before the Ravens came.

Mercia and then Northumbria went up in flames instead. It was the turn of Burnred, Alfred's brother-in-law, to pay the Dane geld. Twice he had appealed to Wessex for aid, but this time he knew that Wessex had no aid to give. He fled to Rome and died there a few weeks later.

Mercia lay completely in the Northmen's power, but they chose to leave it nominally in English hands, setting up a Mercian noble as a puppet King to do their will in all things. But there was worse to come. The vast Danish War Host divided into two, the first host under Halfdan, marched north to finish once and for all the conquest of Northumbria, while the second, under three leaders, Guthrum, Oscytel and Anund, headed for the Cambridgeshire fens. The terror of Halfdan's host spread through the north until it reached even remote Lindisfarne, the Sanctuary of St Cuthbert, and the monks took up the Saint's bones and at low tide carried them across the sandy causeway that linked the Holy Island to the Mainland, and away on their homeless wanderings in search of another refuge. The other host was still spreading fire and terror through the fens a year later, and while Alfred and his best troops were out after them, a great company of Danes got through their guard in the dark of an autumn night, and rode across Wessex to capture the town of Wareham, commanding the Isle of Purbeck and strong behind its turf ramparts.

Once again, Alfred had to pay the Danes geld. But this time at least the Danes gave him the hostages he demanded, and swore to abide by their side of the bargain on Thor's arm-ring lying on the altar of their Gods. It was the first time they had ever bound themselves by that oath, save among their own people, and it may have seemed to Alfred that there was hope at last.

The hope guttered out soon enough. Within a year the Danes had broken their word and were away westward towards Exeter. Alfred went after them with all the troops that he could gather quickly from winter quarters, but could not come up with them before they gained the shelter of the old red walls. This time, however, all was not well with the Northmen. The Saxon army was in winter camp outside the walls, with the countryside to supply them, and the Danish fleet, which had sailed from its old moorings at Sandwich to support them, was caught in a mighty storm and driven on to jagged cliffs on the Dorset coast, with the loss of a hundred and twenty ships. And so they made another peace, and this time kept their bargain, by disappearing over the border into Mercia again.

But there was little respite for the Saxons. Wessex was an island surrounded on all sides by either the sea or the enemy and it was now that Alfred, understanding the potency of sea-power as no Saxon had ever done before, began to build ships: 'Nearly twice as long as those of the Danes, and swifter and steadier and higher, some with sixty oars and some with more; not built after the Frisian manner nor after the Danish, but as seemed best and most useful to the King himself.'

The Danes did not bide quiet in Mercia, but in a short while came pouring south again, to Chippenham in Wiltshire, from which their raiding became so terrible that many of the north Wiltshire folk fled overseas, or even gave themselves and their land up to the invaders in despair, believing that all was over, and England lost beyond saving. Early that year, too, a younger brother of Halfdan's, with twenty-three ships from the Norse settlements in South Wales, began raids on the Devon coast. Wessex was melting, crumbling day by day like a sand fortress where the tide comes in.

Alfred did not believe that England was lost, but to seek to hold the crumbling sand fortress would be only to be washed away at last with no good purpose served. Soon after Easter he gathered his household warriors and the pick of what remained of the War Host, and with Ethelnoth Aelderman of Somerset, who had long been a close friend of his, disappeared into the Parratt Marshes, to the Isle of Athelney.

It is strange to remember that in this desperate time, he must have been back in the country in which Arthur made his last stand, and maybe above the marshes and the reed beds and the willows, the apple trees were breaking into flower at Avalon.

The marshes are well drained now, save for those parts which are used for growing basket willows, but it must have been a desperate place enough in Alfred's day, lowered over by wide stormy skies in winter, a breeding place for fever in the summer, soundless save for the wind in the reeds and alder scrub, and the

45

whistle of the wild geese overhead. But the higher ground in the midst of it offered refuge, and a time to gather strength again. Here, where the Danes had never penetrated, Alfred raised a strongly stockaded fort. There was little difficulty as to food, for deer and rooting wild pig roamed the higher fringes of the land, and there was wild fowl for the snaring, and the island farms and holdings were the homes of men who, though they were desperately poor, were loyal and hardy, willing to share what they had with the King and his men, and teach them the hidden ways through the marshes.

There, in his fastness, as the summer weeks went by, Alfred made what plans he could, and from there he sent out the war bands to meet the Danish raiding parties, and messengers who carried his orders and kept him in touch with his aeldermen and captains all across what yet remained of Wessex. From here, too, his most trusted men went out disguised as tinkers and herdsmen and wandering minstrels, to play the spy in the Danish camps. Alas, the story of how Alfred himself went to the Danes disguised as a harper, is all legend. No word was ever heard of it before the writings of William of Malmsbury in the twelfth century, and the story of his burning the cakes is almost certainly legend too. They are the stories that gather to the Hero's name; but they are legends which illumine Alfred's character. They are what they are because he was what he was, fearless and filled with initiative, and the sort of man who could sit at a peasant's hearth, bearing himself not as a King but simply as a man beneath another man's roof.

From this time forward, Halfdan, Oscytel and Anund disappear from the story and no one knows what became of them, and Alfred is left to face one great Danish leader, Guthrum.

And against Guthrum he sallied out from his marshland fortress at Ascensiontide. At 'Egbert's Stone' on the borders of Wiltshire, where he had appointed the meeting place, he raised once more the Red Dragon of Wessex that (though few would have remembered it) had been the Red Dragon of Britain. And there on that day of early summer, there gathered to him all the men of Wiltshire and Somerset who could still bear arms, and many from the Hampshire forests, even their women, and boys not yet come to the legal age to bear arms. They greeted him as though he were back from the dead, thronging about him, clinging to his feet in the stirrups, shouting for him with a great joy that his heart must have been almost split in two to hear. That night they camped where they were. Next morning they marched; *that* night they camped in Southleigh Wood, and towards evening of the next day, came to Edington hard by Westbury, high in the slow green Wiltshire downs. Here the Danes under Guthrum met him, and as Asser tells in his *Life* Alfred he

> Closed his ranks, shield locked with shield, and fought fiercely against the entire heathen host in long and stubborn stand. At last by God's will he won his victory, slew very many, and pursued the rest to their place of refuge, striking as he went. All things he came upon outside this shelter, men and horses and cattle he made his own. The men he killed, the beasts he captured, and then pitched camp boldly with all his army before the gates of the fortress held by the heathen.

For a fortnight Alfred blockaded the Northmen in their stronghold at Chippenham, some fifteen miles from the battle, until, starving, and with no ships now to give them hope of relief, they surrendered. They made the usual promises to leave Wessex in peace, and again yielded up hostages for their good faith, but this time there was something else. For three weeks later, with twenty-nine chosen captains of his army, the great Viking Guthrum was baptised into the Christian Church, Alfred standing as his God-father.

This wholesale conversion of a defeated people always seems an odd thing; one is supposed to believe that it is a true conversion, but it always has the look of a thing done to order. And that is exactly what it was. It was the final submission of the conquered to the conqueror.

Over and over again it happened. Sometimes the conversion became genuine later as an acquired habit. Sometimes the new Christian merely added Christ to the company of his own gods; sometimes he went wholeheartedly back to the old gods the moment it was safe to do so; sometimes as time went on, he became filled with a burning sincerity for his new faith. But always in the first place the thing was purely a matter of conquest, a political and not a spiritual thing.

As a Christian, Guthrum swore his covenant to lead the Grand Army out of Wessex, and cease the harrying of Alfred's territories. He marched northward and made his camp at Cirencester, and while he was there another fleet of Danish ships anchored in the Thames. Anxious days followed, but though Guthrum and these new Viking leaders actually met, the fleet sailed again, while Guthrum and his men moved back to East Anglia. Probably he thought it would be better to wait until he had strengthened his hold on the east-coast counties by settling Danish farmers there as he had already done in Mercia and Northumbria, before he tried oath breaking with Alfred again.

For two years Wessex was at peace, until in 884 more Northmen poured in from overseas, to lay siege to Rochester. All that winter the townsfolk held out, until in the first days of spring Alfred came to their relief, and the Vikings fled to their ships, leaving behind them all the horses they had brought from the Continent, to fall to the Saxons as the prize of victory. This news was too much for Guthrum who at once forgot his oath and took up again the old war with Wessex. And now, Alfred's new navy proved its worth, for he was able to send every seaworthy ship that he could muster, to deal with the Danish fleet off the East Anglian coast. The Saxon fleet met sixteen of the black Danish warships off the mouth of the Stour, and after a fine fierce battle, took all of them captive with everything and every soul on board. But as the Saxon fleet, heavy laden, was ploughing home, Guthrum in his turn gathered every Viking ship within his reach, and unleashed them after the Saxons. Sailing light, they overhauled their quarry, and in the battle that followed, the Saxons lost all that they had won.

But there was one battle still to be fought. Roused to cold fury by this defeat after his victories, determined to strike once and for all, before the fortunes of war could begin to swing against him once more, Alfred, who had already called out the Fyrd to march on East Anglia, marched instead with a great burning of Viking-held towns, upon London itself. And when it was his, and a smoking ruin full of dead men, he handed it over to be rebuilt and justly ruled over, to his greatest friend, Ethelred, Aelderman of Mercia.

When Guthrum again sought peace, he found he had a harder man to deal with than he had had before. And the peace that he got was a different one, with far more definite terms.

England was now divided into two, Saxon and Danish. Alfred left the Danish free to govern their own part as they would, so long as they kept to their own frontiers and to the terms of the treaty; and he himself ruled the south, with the western midlands and English Mercia held for him by Ethelred.

So the long struggle was over, and Alfred's Kingdom had taken the shape it was to hold for so many years.

Much had been lost but very much had been saved. And under Alfred's shield there was peace in England. And for the King there was time at last to turn from war to matters which, magnificent soldier though he was, were dearer to his heart than the art of fighting had ever been.

He found himself with a land whose towns were half in ruins, whose people, after so many years of war, had forgotten how to live after the ways of peace. He set to work to build a Government, he made laws to deal with the lawlessness left behind, he caused the towns to be rebuilt, trade to be set going again; he saw to the upkeep of the Navy he had created, both the ships and the men. Sometimes he even found time for beauty, for the flash of goldsmith's work, the coloured glow of illuminated vellum in fine books, for the strange sinuous birds carved upon the keystone of a cathedral's arched doorway.

It was his sorrow that his country was steeped in ignorance after a century in which English learning had shone through Europe. And he set to work to improve his own rather faulty Latin so that he could himself translate—and oversee the translating of other men—many books into English, that his people might read them in their own tongue. He worked harder in the years of peace than he had ever done in the years of war, for in the fighting-times there had always been breathing spaces between whiles. Now, there were no breathing spaces. He reduced his sleep to five hours a night; he wore himself out in the loving service of his people, and died before his fiftieth birthday.

Alfred was as great a man in peace as he was in war, maybe greater. But people are choosy and unreasonable in the things that they remember about their Heroes, because they remember with their hearts and not their minds. And so we think of him chiefly, not as a law-maker and administrator and translator of many books in the long night hours when his over-driven body cried out for rest, but as he stands, sculptured in bronze, with all his war gear on him, his great shield at his feet and his sword naked in his hand, gazing down the long High Street of Winchester, the ancient capital of his England.

Chapter 4

Hereward

Two hundred more summers go by, two hundred times the wild geese come down from the north at the start of winter, and again a great danger gathers over England, and again a Hero rises.

Hereward of Mercia is the least of the Heroes so far, but he was well enough loved in his day, for the legends to gather to him as they did to Arthur before him and Robin Hood afterwards.

It is not certain who he was, but tradition makes him son to Earl Leofric of Mercia and his wife—that Lady Godiva who saved the oppressed citizens of Coventry by her famous and spectacular ride. The gentle and pious mother, it seems, singled out her beloved second son to become a monk, but if so, she must have had a pathetic trust in miracles, and she must very soon have realised that the necessary miracle was not going to take place in Hereward's case, for the picture of Hereward that emerges from the many stories about him, could not by any means be fitted into the rigid discipline of a monastic life. Indeed any kind of discipline was quite outside his nature. He was as wild as a hawk; a big-boned, golden-headed lad with one blue eye and one grey, and a temper as wayward and ready to flare as thicket-fire in a dry summer.

At sixteen he captained a band of kindred spirits, and from his father's hall at Bourne, they terrorised the Fen Country for miles around. But there was never any malice in his devilry; he thought nothing of holding up some rich merchant for the gold he had on him, but he always made good the loss afterward; he played rough tricks on the monks of Ely Priory, but took his punishment cheerfully when it came. It was the adventure he wanted, the fun of the fight, the triumph of some skilful and daring plan carried successfully through. He would have stolen the father prior's hair shirt off his back for a wager, and given it back to him with a gold piece for the poor tied in the sleeve, simply for the fun of doing it.

Small wonder that when her Lord was at home, the Lady

Godiva spent much of her time in standing between them, desperately trying to curb her wild son and soothe his father. And when Leofric, who spent much of his time in the household of the King, sent for his son to attend him at Court, she must have begged the boy to behave himself, and seen him go with the deepest foreboding of trouble to come.

It was not long in coming.

Hereward found the Court of Edward the Confessor not much to his taste. He called the King 'The Miracle Monger' almost to his face, and carried on blithely the feud with the sons—Harold especially—of Earl Godwin of Kent, which their two proud fathers had begun long since in their questing after power. He hated the Norman favourites who even then surrounded the King; he made his own private war on them, a war that was more than half in scornful jest, but had results that were serious enough. For the Normans complained furiously of his horse-play to the Confessor who was shocked to his spinsterish soul, and finally, after he had used his enormous physical strength to toss one of the Norman nobles on to the hall roof for the pleasure of watching him roll off again into the muck-heap piled against the wall, Hereward was summoned to the King's presence, and before the whole Council, including Earl Leofric and Earl Godwin, he was solemnly exiled, his father saying no word in his defence.

Hereward thanked the King (one can hear the defiance and the hearty scorn in his voice). He had fretted for years against the dull peace of the realm, now the world was his for wandering over and his fortune waiting to be won at his sword's point. 'Only when I am gone, all you grave and noble sirs, pray that you never need the strength of my arm. For if the day comes that you do, it may be that you will call for me, and it may be that I will not come!'

So Hereward (there is no trace of his ever having been nick-named the Wake during his lifetime or for many years afterward) rode away into exile.

He did not leave England at once, but headed first for Northumbria, where old Earl Siward ruled almost like an independent king and the Confessor's writ of exile counted for very little. His Godfather Gilbert, who held York and was one of the richest Thanes in England, was also Lord of Ghent, for already there were men who held land and title on both sides of the Narrow Seas; and he kept many young men in his household, Norman, Fleming and Saxon, who came to him for training in arms and courtesy. Gilbert received him warmly, and gave him a place among the rest, from which he soon rose by daring and laughter and the strength of his fist, to be cock of the walk.

It is to this time, and the timber castle among the northern heather that one of the legends belongs, a good legend and worth the telling, whether or not there is any truth in it.

Gilbert of Ghent, so the story runs, had in his steading a great polar bear, huge and dangerous, and kept in a barred den. The dread that all men had of it was more than mortal, for they called it The Fairy Bear, and it was commonly supposed to be blood-kin in some strange and terrible way to old Earl Siward, who carried a bear for his badge and had had something of the polar bear's treacherous ferocity in his youth.

One morning, when Gilbert was from home, Hereward, returning from a morning ride heard the most hideous uproar bursting from the inner courtyard. He dropped from his horse in the outer garth and ran for the gateway and what he saw as he strode through made him check and urge it quickly to behind him. There, outside the shattered bars of the den, a few links of broken chain dangling from his neck, stood the Fairy Bear. His head was lowered and swung slowly from side to side, small as a snake's compared to the rest of his body, deadly menace in every line of him as he looked round with little red angry eyes. The door of the hall was fast shut, and from behind it came a splurging of voices and the screams of a woman having hysterics. And alone in the otherwise empty courtyard, a girl of twelve or so, who he knew for Elftruda, one of those who waited on the Lady of the Castle as he did on the Lord, was pressed against the door, beating on it with her clenched fists and crying piteously to those beyond to open and let her in for the love of God. While all the time she stared over her shoulder with huge, terrified eyes.

Only a greater babble of voices from inside answered her, and even as Hereward let the pin of the gate fall behind him, the great beast, irritated by all the noise and by his dangling chain, let out a deep sound that was more like an angry cough than the growl of a bear, and made a rush towards the girl.

Hereward gave a yell to distract the brute's attention, and sprang forward into the path of the lumbering charge, freeing as he did so the war axe he had been using earlier that morning at practice, and which still hung at his belt. The Fairy Bear swung towards him, and Hereward crouched and side-sprang, swinging the axe round his head, and brought it whistling down to split the flat skull of the beast, which lurched and rolled over without a sound.

52

Next instant Elftruda was in his arms, shaken with sobs as she clung to him. The young man, who was like one of those great fierce clumsy hounds that are always gentle with children, hugged her close. 'See! It's all over and the beast is dead! No cause for all this weeping!' and then as she grew calmer he asked 'What happened here?'

'We were all out here watching a pair of strolling tumblers', said Elftruda, 'and the pipe music must have angered the Fairy Bear for he broke the bars of his den and came charging out with his chain hanging about his neck; and everybody ran but I was the furthest from the hall and they were so frightened that they crashed shut the door and left me still outside!'

'The cowards!' said Hereward. 'They deserve payment for that!' and his odd eyes began to dance. His own young groom had come after him from the outer court. 'Martin, help me with this carcass——'

The groom hurried to help him, grinning, and between them, while Elftruda looked on in mingled terror and delight, they dragged the great yellow-white carcass against the wall with its bloody muzzle within a handspan of the door-opening. Then he called to those within, still panting with his efforts, 'All's safe. You can come out now.'

There was a burst of voices behind the door, and after a long pause, the door opened, only to crash shut again as the man who had opened it saw the Fairy Bear seemingly about to thrust inside, and sprang back with a howl of fear.

Hereward even went so far as to send the bear's body thundering against the door, for the pleasure of hearing those within cry upon the saints to save them. Then, growing tired of the joke, he dragged the great carcass outside again and gave the door a hearty and unmistakable human kick, letting loose a gale of pent-up laughter as he called to the people in the hall to come out and choose their own bear-steaks for supper, or bide within while he kicked Gilbert's fine painted door down if that pleased them better.

And when at last they summoned up courage to open the door again, there stood Hereward with his bloody axe in his hand and the dead bear outstretched at his feet, and the maiden Elftruda hovering gleefully behind him. And at sight of their faces he flung back his head and howled and whooped with laughter, until there was scarcely a man there who would not gladly have knifed him where he stood.

After that, Hereward was the darling and the hero of every

woman and girl in Gilbert's castle, and of all the humble folk round about; but the Normans and Flemings hated him so well that they planned among themselves how to kill him. He would not have left the castle for anything that they might do, but he could not help feeling that if the Fairy Bear was really some kin to Siward, the old Earl might well seek vengeance for the beast's death. Also by that time he was tired of his Godfather's stronghold, and the itch for wandering was on him again, so he bade farewell to Sir Gilbert of Ghent, and to the maiden Elftruda—a little sadly to Elftruda, for she was very pretty, and if she had been only two or three years older she would have been worth falling in love with. And with Martin Lightfoot he set forth again on his travels.

This time he took ship for Ireland; later, he was in Cornwall, and legends have grown around his time in both places, of how, amongst other things, he befriended a Cornish Princess and an Irish Viking Chief in their love for each other—in the cause of which he entered the enemy camp in the guise of a harper. The same story has already done duty for Alfred.

From Cornwall he went to Flanders, to put his sword at the service of Count Baldwin, Gilbert's kinsman. He must, for all the dangers and troubles of his life, have been one of those people who always fall cat-like on their feet, for the next time we hear of him, he is married to a maiden of the Court at Bruges, Torfrida by name, beautiful, clever, gentle, and very rich in her own right.

The years passed and he was no longer a boy, but a man in his full strong prime, a man like a west wind and a thundercloud and a burst of sunshine all rolled into one; when there began to be the first stirrings of a Norman invasion of England. Word of Duke William's plans must have reached Flanders before England heard it, and for the first time Hereward behaved in a way that would seem to run counter to his own nature. One would expect him to be away back to his own country with his sword naked in his hand. Instead, he stayed quietly in Flanders, watching, and doing nothing. True, he had suffered banishment and given the English King and his Council fair warning. 'It may be that you will call to me, and it may be that I will not come.' But he was not a man to let mere banishment stand in his way at such a time, and one can only think that it was his personal hatred of the new King—for the Confessor was dead, and Harold the son of Earl Godwin had come to the throne—that held him back from giving his support. The power of the blood-feud was terribly strong in Hereward's day, as the power of the vendetta is in the Sicily of our own. But if he would not join shields with Harold Godwinson in defence of his own land, neither would he march with Duke William in the ranks of the invaders. So he stayed in Flanders, this wildest and most headstrong of the Saxon nobles; let his sword bide in its sheath, and waited. Even news of his father's death did not bring him home.

It was not until the Conqueror had been crowned more than a year, and Harold more than a year dead at Senlac, that news of how things were going in England at last brought him back.

By then the Saxon estates were being handed out to their new Norman Lords, and among them, Bourne, his own home in Lincolnshire had fallen to the lot of a Norman knight. News of this he heard from old friends who he went to after landing on the Lincolnshire coast, and from them too, he heard how the man had ill-treated and humiliated his mother and the rest of the household. 'Let him kick my folk and swill my beer while he can', said Hereward. 'He shall pay his reckoning in a while and a while'.

At first he seemed to do little. He spoke to a young Thane here and an old basket-weaver there, and waited quietly by his friend's fire, with his sword still sheathed, but loose in its sheath. No word of his coming reached the Norman overlord, but among his own people it spread, quietly and swiftly, by the winding waterways and through alder thickets, from village to village, from fisherman's bothie to charcoal burner's hut, to small manor lost in the marshes, still in Saxon hands. And soon, men began to gather by night to the appointed meeting place. In ones and twos the band of wild lads who had terrorised the countryside with him, gathered again, grown men now and with a new purpose in their hearts; humble folk too, to serve him as men-at-arms. And so at last, with a sizeable war band behind him, Hereward came home.

The Normans were making merry in the Hall of Bourne that night, the blurred uproar of their voices, raised to drown the soughing of the autumn wind across the marshes, drowned too any sound of the Saxons closing in—until the very moment when the gate burst open and Hereward and his war band were upon them.

Hardly one Norman escaped that night's work, to carry word of it to their own Lord, Ivo de Taillebois at Spalding.

With Bourne once more in his own hands, Hereward set his mother back in her rightful place, and leaving a garrison of his own men to keep all safe, returned to Bruges to fetch Torfrida, and having done so, placed her in the safety of the nunnery at Peterborough, where his mother later joined her. There was to be no place for women in his life for the next few years.

Of Torfrida, swept away by this wild west wind of a man from the Court at Bruges to the cold thin life of waiting, in a Fenland nunnery, we hear no more. Whether Hereward visited her there, often at first, and then less and less often, and whether, for the sake of these visits, she counted everything else well lost; even whether she died in Peterborough, or grew at last weary beyond endurance of the waiting, and went back to her own people, and the world he had taken her from, all that is lost. From the moment that the nunnery doors closed behind her, there is nothing more to tell of the flower of the Flemish Court.

During the months that followed, Hereward made his presence powerfully felt among the Normans of the Fen Country. He set up a refuge camp on the Isle of Ely, where folk driven from their homes by the new masters could find shelter, and with his steadily increasing war bands, harried those new masters by every means in his power, so that even on the furthest fringes of the countryside they scarcely dared lie down to sleep at night save with their swords naked in their hands.

Ivo de Taillebois himself was one of the worst of his kind, and his kind was the jumped-up rich who had none of the sense of rough justice, the courage in oneself that recognises courage in others, none of the acceptance of a knight's obligations or the tradition of land-holding behind him that were the harsh virtues of many of the Conqueror's companions. He found sport in letting his men torment the poorer Saxons, in loosing his hounds on them and their flocks, lamed their cattle or had them thrown into the river to drown, in mere idle sport, and thought nothing of firing a farmhouse roof because some wretched villain had looked him too straight in the eye for his pleasure. And the new holders of the Lincolnshire manors took their tone from their overlord. So that Hereward, in that first year or so, found many debts to pay on behalf of his own folk, and paid them nobly.

He had time for settlements of his own, too, as when he challenged Frederick Warenne, who had been foremost in snatching Bourne from its true lord, to trial by combat according to 'The Wager of Battle'. Frederick refused the challenge on the grounds that Hereward was no dubbed knight. (He had in fact been knighted on his return to England, but by a churchman, which the Normans refused to recognise as legal knighthood.) Hereward, not being minded to take no for an answer, bearded him in his manor and forced him to accept the challenge and killed him before his own courtyard gates.

Soon after that, the Conqueror, who seems at times to have had a rough sense of humour that might well match Hereward's own, hearing that Thorold, Abbot of Malmsbury was for ever at daggers drawn with his English monks, and that he kept a large band of men-at-arms to enforce his rule, said, 'I'll find him his match!' and promptly gave orders that he should be transferred to Peterborough. The monks of Peterborough, knowing their new Abbot's reputation for gold-greed as well as tyranny, appealed to Hereward to save the Abbey treasures for them, and he, with great goodwill, carried off every silver cup and gold-embroidered alb to safekeeping in Ely. Thorold, arriving in Peterborough soon after, with one hundred and fifty men-at-arms, immediately joined forces with de Taillebois to recover them. But Hereward was indeed a match for the Lord Abbot. By mounting a mock attack he drew off de Taillebois' men, and while they were well and truly lost in the marshes, himself captured the Abbot, and made him pay £2,500 ransom before letting him go again.

By this time the resistance leader with the odd eyes was becoming master of the Fen Country. He had formed his own personal band of household warriors, which included old friends and two young nephews, Siward the Red and Siward the White, and to him there gathered a growing host of Thanes, freemen, and peasants, all eager to strike for their own fields and their freedom. The monastery itself served them for headquarters, where ring-shirted warriors and brown-robed monks sat side by side in the refectory with shields and weapons hanging ready on the walls behind them. But soon there were too many for the monastery to hold and they had to camp round about it, as whole war bands began to come in from further and further afield. The warrior Bishop of Durham, and the Abbot of St Albans, each with a following of men-at-arms, the tenants of St Mary of Abingdon, a band of men from Berkshire; steadily the army of resistance grew, until there were close on four thousand men among the woods and marshes.

The Normans knew that the time had come when they must move against Hereward as against a hostile nation on the war trail. William de Warenne, Lord of Lewes, with his brother Frederick's blood to avenge, brought up his feudal levies to join de Taillebois at Spalding. William Malet and other Norman chiefs followed and lastly the Conqueror himself brought up his army, raised his standard at Cambridge and took over the command. To begin with, he started a strict blockade, but though that could hinder to inflow of arms and war supplies, food was another matter. Both fish and wild fowl were easily got, and as had been the case with Alfred in Athelney, the fisher's and country folk were Hereward's to a man; sheep and cattle, barley and rye had been got in from the country round, and the Saxon stronghold was ready for a long struggle.

The Normans could gain no footing in the Isle of Ely, until at last the King ordered a causeway to be built across the Ouse at Aldrett. Stones, tree-trunks and even oxhides were used in the construction, the road builders working under the protecting cover of bands of archers and men-at-arms, and as soon as it was completed, an attack in force was made along it. But the defenders drove the Normans back again and again, until they began to think that magic was at work, and King William had the happy thought of making a kind of movable wooden tower, putting a witch in it, and trundling her ahead of his troops to fight the defender's magic with her own. But even this had no effect. Hereward and his men surrounded the tower, killed its guards and burned it down with the wretched witch still inside it.

Hereward, who was so unlike Alfred in most ways, was like him in being a born soldier with a genius for strategy and for seizing an opportunity. Under pressure of this enemy who so greatly outnumbered his own force, he held to a strictly defensive role, but whenever the chance came for action, he struck out with blasting strength. He possessed also the faculty of forethought that many a later general lacked, not only of always having men in the right place at the right moment, but boats, horses and supplies also. His old fierce delight in a boy's adventure never forsook him in this grimmer man's business of driving back at sword-point the flower of the Norman chivalry. And his own spirit kept up the spirit of his men so that despite the hardships and the constant fighting, the heart of the whole camp was high. That was so at least of the fighting men, but for the monks of Ely it was different. They were used to austerity but not to this pinching hardship and constant sharp edge of danger; and moreover, William had seized all the Abbey lands, and there was only one way to get them back again.

Treachery was suddenly among them, only a thought at first, but growing in strength until suddenly it was an accomplished fact. A band of them stole out one night and made their way to the Norman camp. They knew the secret ways across the marshes, and they betrayed them to the enemy.

So the Normans, with the secret ways now open to them, attacked again—and took the Saxons by surprise. A thousand of Hereward's men fell in that fight among the marshy fringes of Ely, and the traitor monks were repaid by having forty men-at-arms quartered on them for many years to come.

Hereward and his household warriors, after seeing the rest safely dispersed, fell back to the ships they had in waiting. It was time to abandon Ely, now that the secret ways were Norman property. He retired on his old home at Bourne. Oger the Breton, a distant kinsman, had been given the Bourne estates, but seems to have yielded them up to their rightful owner without a blow struck on either side. And at Bourne, in the midst of Morkary Woods, he set about the task of gathering his War Host again.

The woods that he had known from boyhood as a fox knows its own runs, made as good a base for his operations as ever the Isle of Ely had done. The herdsmen's bothies, put up and shifted from week to week gave his men shelter, and in the forest ways any Norman force that came too close could be quite conveniently ambushed, so that before long the Conqueror's men came to fear Morkary Woods as the haunt of devils. From these headquarters, Hereward carried on a fierce and successful guerrilla warfare, ranging further and further as time went by through all the counties of Mercia. No force, it seemed, could cope with his speed of movement; his war bands that appeared out of the moorland mist and melted into the forest shadows when their red work was done. It seemed nothing for him and his mounted bands to cover thirty or forty miles in a night, attack some Norman outpost at dawn, scatter its defenders and carry off any that seemed worth holding to ransom, and be safely back in his own woods before the next day dawned.

The final burst of triumph came when he captured Ivo de Taillebois and in that very triumph lay the beginning of the sorry end to this story.

De Taillebois was too powerful, too close to the King, to be left in rebel Saxon hands, and Hereward, knowing it, made a use of his captive so astonishing that it strikes one like a douche of cold water in the face.

He used him as a bargaining counter, to make peace with the Conqueror!

It was the only sensible thing to do. There was no future in the resistance; it could make life a burden to the Normans, but never drive them back across the Narrow Seas. His war bands were many, but ill-armoured by comparison with the Norman men-at-arms, and maybe beginning to suffer from privation and old wounds, whereas the Normans grew stronger year by year.

William, on his side, probably realised that there would be no holding England in peace while Hereward and his war bands kept up the resistance. So negotiations began, and ended with Hereward's lands restored to him, while he swore fealty for them to the King, like any Norman baron.

Soon after, he was married again, this time to a girl of his own race, who brought him a knight's fee in land at Evenlode in Worcestershire, and settled down with her to breed sons.

Once again he took to the war trail, when in 1074 he went with King William on his expedition to Maine, in command of the Saxon Fyrd in the army of the King. For the rest, he sank quietly out of history, and died as old men die, in his bed.

But the true end of the story is long before, and the Hereward of the Hero-tale dies in that moment of capturing Ivo de Taillebois. Of all the Heroes in this book, he is the only one whose light goes out before his death, leaving him with half his life still to live as no more than a man among other men. To make peace with William was the sensible thing to do; it was even best for his people in the long run. But people seldom care very greatly what is good for them, and sensibleness is not one of the qualities that make a Hero. Nor is a quiet old age, and what the stern fighting men of his own day and breed still felt in their heart of hearts to be 'a straw death' and not a warrior's.

So strong was this feeling among his own people, that among the legends that began within forty years to be woven around his name, was one that gave him a death more worthy of his young days, a death that his people felt he ought to have had; cut down fighting like a boar at bay, during a Norman attack on his hall. He slays four of the enemy before his sword breaks on the head of a fifth, then, seizing his shield in both hands, he crushes two more with it before he goes down at last, overwhelmed by numbers.

Alas, it was the straw death that was the true one.

Chapter 5

Llewellin

Except possibly, for Robin Hood, the line of English Heroes—
or the Heroes of what we now call England—is ended, and the
tale is taken up by the mountain people and the hillmen of the
north and west. It is a strange fact that all migrations, all things
that have to do with the soul and the legends of a people rise in
the east and travel towards the west.

Arthur is dead in Somerset, Alfred in Winchester, Hereward in
his Worcestershire manor, Caratacus in exile in far-off Rome, and
with Henry III on the English throne, the Prince Llewellin,
the last champion but one, of Welsh freedom, stands up in
Gwynedd, on the heights of Snowdon, and loosens his sword
in its sheath.

Llewellin Ap Gryffyd, grandson of Llewellin the Great, Prince
of North Wales, was only a boy when his father died in trying to
escape from an English prison; still only a boy when his uncle
Davydd who had succeeded to the Princedom, also died in 1246,
and the rule descended to him and his brother Owain, called
Owain Goch, from the red colour of his hair. It was decided that
they should divide the land equally between them, but while they
were busy with the division, Henry's Seneschal seized the southern
dependencies of the Princedom, and Maelgwn Vichan, their
princeling, fled to Gwynedd for help. The two brothers, not yet
out of their teens, found themselves on the edge of war with
England, and for the first of many times, took to the mountains.
The trouble was patched up, and the young Princes, though with
hot and angry hearts, performed their homage to Henry III at
Woodstock. They received the King's pardon for sheltering his
enemies on terms which show how low the Welsh Royal House
had fallen since the days of their mighty grandfather. He had
died lord of almost all Wales; *they* went back from Woodstock
with nothing left to them but Snowdon and Anglesey, while
England pouched all the rest. One can imagine the despairing
fury of the two young eagles, mewed up in the narrow confines of

62

Gwynedd and the vows they must have made to break out one day and retake all that their grandfather had once held.

The English King left them in peace, for they had not the strength to be any danger to him. But between themselves there was no peace. Fierce red Prince and fierce black were too closely thrust together for that and each lived, as it were, with his hand on his dagger. Owain was the eldest, but Llewellin was the strongest, and soon thrust into the lead, and held it for seven years, until Owain with a younger brother Davydd finally rose against him in open rebellion. Both sides called in their own followers, there was a pitched battle, and Llewellin, the victor, took his brother Owain captive and held him for more than twenty years, while Davydd fled to England to put himself under the protection of the King. Llewellin was left alone as Prince of Gwynedd.

And alone he set out on the re-conquest of all that his grandfather had once held. At once, the lesser chieftains began to fear this new power that had risen among them. Some even went over to English Henry, and Henry, thinking to strengthen the English hold on Wales before the situation got out of hand, made his eldest son Edward, Earl of Chester, and granted him all the lands held by the Crown in Wales. The new young Earl made his power felt without delay by setting his bailiffs on to make a survey of the lands and castles, even in Gwynedd itself; also he tried to set up in the south a shire-system with English laws, to oust the Welsh local customs. A cry of fury rose at once throughout South Wales, and instantly the Prince Llewellin called out his war bands and flung himself out to champion the Welsh cause.

In 1256, he carried desolation to the very gates of Chester, then turning south into what later became Cardigan, he boldly granted the lands that Prince Edward held there, to a vassal of his own. He drove out the great Marcher Lord, Roger Mortimer (who was, incidentally, a kinsman of his despite the difference of race between them), forced the Lord of Powys to take refuge in England, and in the following Lent, marched triumphantly into South Wales. He spent most of Lent on the Bristol Channel coast, burning out the English lords of Kidwelly, Gower and Swansea, and at Easter, turned north again laden with booty from the land whose overlords had yielded to him as a conqueror while its own people rose to greet him as a deliverer.

All Prince Edward's plans had been smashed and the King his father had not moved to help him. But when, late that summer, news reached the English Court that Llewellin had taken league with the nobles of Scotland, Henry did move at last, and with Prince Edward, marched into North Wales. But even then he never crossed the Conway, and so his expedition had no effect on Llewellin's territories. He could not dare the wilds of Snowdonia without a promised force from Ireland to strengthen his own, and though he waited more than a month for it, it never came and he was forced at last to fall back into England, leaving the countryside again open to Llewellin, who followed hard on his heels, cutting off stragglers so successfully that next year the barons refused to follow the King on another Welsh campaign at all.

The border struggle continued, and beside the English, Llewellin still had to cope with rival Welsh chieftains. But already men were marvelling how this wild mountain Prince was yoking all warring Wales together into a workable if unruly team.

And meanwhile, in England, the trouble was beginning to brew between the King and his barons led by Simon de Montfort, his brother-in-law. The Marcher Lords were strongly for the King, and Llewellin therefore took his stand with de Montfort in his struggle for a people's Parliament. The Welsh Prince did not care a straw in the wind how England was governed, but de Montford was closely allied with the young Earl of Gloucester, and so by throwing in his lot with them, he could face Edward or the King with more strength at his back than ever before.

By April of 1263 the Barons' War had broken out and the King had other work on his hands, so Prince Edward was left to deal with the Welsh hornets' nest on his own and as yet it was a task beyond him. The castles of Diserth, Radnor, and Deganwy, the strongest castle in North Wales, were in Llewellin's hands and Edward had no choice but to call a truce.

Early next year, the final desperate struggle of the Barons' War began, and in May, Henry was defeated at Lewes and Prince Edward taken captive. Just a year later, young Edward escaped to gather the Marcher Lords behind him and the war was on again; but at first the Barons had the best of things and at Hereford in June, King Henry was forced to grant Llewellin the Principality, with the homage of all the Welsh Lords. 'That year,' said the Chronicles, 'the Welsh enjoyed peace from the English, Llewellin, Son of Gwffyd being Prince of all Wales'. At about the same time there began to be a plan between him and de Montfort that he should marry de Montfort's daughter Eleanor. Indeed Llewellin's star was bright in the sky that summer.

But in August, de Montfort met the King's army among the orchards of Evesham, and found there his own death in battle, a

very great man, fighting for what he believed to be right, for the freedom of Englishmen to have a say in their own Government.

The remnant of the Barons' Party still held out against the King, but they were no longer an organised army, only war bands of bold and desperate men among the hills. These, however, were the kind of men most after Llewellin's own heart and it was not long before he had gathered them together and swept them down from the mountains on the war trail again. The King sent a strong force against him, the Pope threatened excommunication. Llewellin laughed and ran the King's Army out of Cheshire.

But despite this brief flare the day was over for de Montfort's party, and with the fall of their dead leader's own castle of Kenilworth, almost their last hope went. At Shrewsbury in later summer, a truce was signed between Llewellin and King Henry. Llewellin was to rule the whole Principality as before, only doing homage for it to the King, while receiving homage in his turn from all the Welsh Barons. He was to pay an indemnity of 24,000 marks and give back all his brother Davydd's lands (which must have hurt like having a tooth drawn!). But none the less, the treaty was considered by both sides to be a victory for the Welsh.

For the rest of Henry's reign, all was quiet along the Marches. But trouble was again brewing under the quiet, as Edward returned to his old plans for making South Wales into shire ground. And the Prince in the high glens of Snowdon bided his time to strike again.

In November 1272, Henry died and Edward was proclaimed King. Llewellin and the new King of England were well matched, eagle against leopard. The breed of Geoffry of Anjou all had something of the big cat in their make-up. It was a brilliant breed, black under the gold, cruel with a leopard's silken cruelty, superbly brave, sometimes a little mad, but with the kind of madness that gets things done; possessed, for the most part, of great personal charm and a gift for fellowship with other men. And in Edward the Angevin blood ran strong.

He was away on a crusade when his reign began, and this gave Llewellin his chance. When he was summoned to take his oath of fealty before the Regents, he did not come, nor did he pay the instalment of his indemnity that had fallen due. Next summer, despite furious protests from the Regents, he started building a new castle almost within sight of the royal stronghold of Montgomerie. He was busy again with the old plan to marry de Montfort's daughter, and he was busy strengthening his own position

66

in Wales by driving out rival or rebellious chieftains, including brother Davydd, who was plotting against him as usual.

When, almost two years after Henry's death, Edward returned to England to be crowned, Llewellin did not attend the Coronation and when summoned to pay his homage (and his debts), took no notice whatever. For one thing, he was busy. War was flaring up again all along the Marches, and he and his wild mountain troops were having fine hunting among the knights and men-at-arms of the Marcher Lords. Summoned a second time, he did reply, begging to be excused, as the fate of his own father, who had obeyed just such a summons to Court and then been seized as a hostage and held through the long years until desperation drove him to the wild attempt to escape that killed him, showed how rash it was to accept such pressing invitations.

One cannot help wondering how this King of the fierce Angevin breed managed to restrain himself from an immediate march on Wales.

He did restrain himself, but he had not long to wait before the chance of a smaller but more amusing revenge for that insult came his way. . . .

The long-drawn negotiations for Llewellin's marriage had just been brought to a finish, and the Lady Eleanor, who was in France, sailed for Wales and her wedding. The King gave his orders accordingly, and off the Scilly Isles just before Christmas, her ship was intercepted and Eleanor was bundled off to Windsor, where she could be kept close under the eye of her aunt the Queen Mother. Llewellin offered the King a large ransom for her release, but Edward was not interested in ransoms; his price was the Welshman's instant and unconditional homage, the return of all the lands he had taken and the rebuilding of the castles he had destroyed. And this, Llewellin flatly refused to consider.

Next autumn, Edward formally declared war on him, appointed Roger Mortimer as his commander, and sent summoning his feudal tenants to meet at Worcester next midsummer. At New Year, he ordered up a strong advance force to hold the Welshman until the time for full invasion came, and soon after Easter he left London to make his base-camp at Shrewsbury for a long campaign.

In the hot days of early August, with the hills shimmering in the summer haze, three great armies poured into Wales, Edward himself leading the northern thrust, the Earl of Lincoln commanding the central force, and still further south, the third army marching under the banners of Edmund of Lancaster.

Llewellin, with no force that could possibly stand against such a three-pronged War Host, had to abandon the southern chieftains to make what terms they could with the Earl of Lancaster. But knowing every inch of the country as he did, he could still carry on a war of sorts, dividing, starving out, and harassing the enemy in a hundred ways. But it was Edward he had to deal with now, not Henry; Edward who was later to be called the Hammer of the Scots; who marched on foot with the army, went tired and thirsty with the least of his men-at-arms and so could lead them as his father had never done. Edward who had the gift of planning larger-than-life, and the ability to carry through his plans, who once felled a whole wood to prevent it giving cover to the Welsh, and brought the whole Cinque Ports Fleet round to patrol the Menai Straits and so cut Gwynedd off from its corn lands of Anglesey.

Llewellin was penned in the mountains, cut off from his food supplies and from all hope of reinforcements, while Edward and his men, having made sure of their own supply lines, sat round Snowdon like hounds round a thicket in which a boar has laired up. The Prince held out until November, and then at last, with his men dying of starvation around him, he came down from the mountains to accept Edward's terms.

They were harder ones, this time, for Edward was determined to show this wild Welshman who was master. Llewellin must surrender all his prisoners, including Owen Goch; once again he was to be stripped of all but the land of Gwynedd; even Anglesey, which had been the corn land of the Lords of Snowdon for a thousand years, he must now pay rent for. His own Welsh lords were called on to renounce him if he broke the treaty, and to make all complete, Owen and Davydd were both given large land-holdings.

But when, at long, long last, Llewellin had sworn homage and so admitted his defeat, Edward showed that he could be at least a little generous, and remitted the rent of Anglesey.

Llewellin spent that Christmas, greatly to his own surprise, at the English Court, and there at last he met the Lady Eleanor. He must have been late in his forties by that time, but the life he had lived was the kind that keeps a man of his sort young and hard and hot-blooded. And even if de Montfort's daughter had been very young when the marriage negotiations started—as many brides of those days were—that had been fifteen years ago, and she could not have been much less than thirty, now, so that maybe he did not seem so old to her, not too old to be a lover. And certainly she seemed fair enough to him. Maybe he had brought his harper with him, to sing her the love songs of his own wild hills, and he had been her father's friend and comrade in a cause that was worth fighting for.

At all events, later into the following summer, when the King and Llewellin met at Worcester to renew the treaty, Eleanor de Montfort was there, too, and in October she and Llewellin were married at the door of Worcester Cathedral, before the Kings of England and Scotland and a great concourse of Lords and Barons. And next day Llewellin carried off his bride to Gwynedd.

The marriage did not last very long. Eleanor had waited so long for this wild black eagle of a husband, and in little over three years she was dead in giving birth to her only child, a daughter who was given the name of Gwenllion, and who fell into the King's power after Llewellin's final downfall, and ended her days as a nun at Sempringham.

The next few years were outwardly peaceful, but under the quiet surface, trouble was brewing again as of old. Llewellin chafed at his loss of power, while Edward's agents carried out roughly and violently his plans for making Wales English, and the Archbishop of Canterbury sought to bring the Welsh Church into line with the English usage with a well-meant heavy-handedness that stirred up first resentment and then open revolt. Llewellin began to listen to the loud complaints of his old subjects who called on him for help against the harsh brutality of the English officials. Edward pressed his legal rights remorselessly, and his henchmen carried out his orders with a ruthlessness that set the whole of Wales smouldering. Even Llewellin's brother Davydd became so disgusted with the English that he secretly made common cause with him against the King. The Welsh chieftains gathered as of old to the Lord of Snowdon, and with a superb recklessness of consequences (did I not say that sensibleness was not one of the qualities that goes to the making of a Hero?) Llewellin roared down from the mountains on his last revolt.

On Palm Sunday eve, 1282, with Davydd at his side, he descended on the Castle of Flint, and within the next few days, on Rhuddlan and Hawarden. He took the castles, and with them Roger Clifford, the King's Lieutenant. Revolt flared through North Wales, and Llewellin swept on through the country, while everywhere men rose joyfully to welcome and join him. And then it was the turn of South Wales.

Edward, the last of his patience chafed raw, had had enough, and resolved, once and for all—no more treaties—to break Llewellin ap Gwffydd and be done with him.

In April, the Welsh Prince was formally excommunicated, and on Midsummer Day, Edward entered Wales at the head of a great and magnificent army. His plan of campaign was the same as before, but on a far greater scale, and to be carried out with far greater ruthlessness. And again Llewellin pulled back into the mountains and was blockaded there both by land and sea. All through the summer Edward was encamped at Conway, while Llewellin clung to his mountain stronghold, flinging off every attack that was launched against him. It was a summer of no pitched battles, but many small-scale raids and skirmishes, a fierce guerrilla warfare that went sometimes one way and sometimes the other. At summer's end, the Archbishop, whose good intentions had done so much to rouse the final revolt, set out for Snowdon alone, carrying the King's terms with him, and spent three days with Llewellin in his stronghold. His offer was that in return for complete submission, Edward would allow his enemy lands in some English county, take charge of his little daughter, and even consider allowing any heir born to him later, to succeed to Snowdon.

Llewellin laughed in his face. And that was the end of negotiating.

The English Army moved in for the kill. The Snowdon passes were closely beset. Llewellin must have known that to try holding out through the winter would be to be forced into surrender. There was only one thing to do. He must escape, break out into the open where he could use the forces that he had, and his superior knowledge of the country. Besides, there was desperate need of him in the south, where Gloucester and Mortimer had won a great victory. Leaving Davydd and most of his followers to carry on the defence of Snowdon, he took with him only a war band of his own household warriors, and by secret mountain ways succeeded in getting out through the besieging English.

Soon after, he burst into view once more, at the head of a small hastily gathered army, devastated Cardigan and then swung Westward to attack the middle Marches. The Welsh tenants of the Mortimer's rose to join him, but even so, with his hurriedly gathered tribesmen, he was no match for the disciplined troops of the Marcher Lords. The thing was hopeless from the start. A final wild throw that he must have known was doomed to failure, by a man choosing to lead a faithful few into one last battle, and go down fighting, rather than yield and live to see Wales and his own neck set under the King's yoke.

No one knows for sure the place of that last battle; it is lost almost as deep as Arthur's Camlan. Somewhere in mid-Wales, near the head waters of the Severn, Edmund Mortimer fell on him, and he was slain by one Adam de Frankton, as he thrust forward into the mêlée.

His mutilated body was buried at Cwmhir, but his head was sent in triumph to London, and set up for a raree-show, on a spearshaft above the ramparts of the Tower, decked with a garland of ivy in mockery for a crown. Not the first Hero's head to be treated so, nor the last.

It might have been better for Wales if he had never been born, but if he had not, the world would have lost something bright and fierce, and Wales herself would have had fewer songs to sing, fewer tales to tell round the fire on winter evenings for the next few hundred years.

Chapter 6

Robin Hood

No book of British Heroes could possibly be complete without
Robin Hood. But *Heroes and History*? Has Robin Hood any
claim to a historical existence? Probably we shall never know now,
for he has got so deeply lost in the mists of legend that he is harder
to find than even Arthur, who is roughly twice as far from us in
time. Some experts trace him back, not to a man at all, but to an
idea; the Spirit of Fertility, green things growing and the rebirth
of spring; the tree Spirit, who, in the form of a man, was sacrificed yearly among primitive peoples, to bring back the growing-
time of the year, and who, bound round with green branches and
coloured ribbons, as 'Jack-in-the-Green', was part of so many
May Day merrymakings even into this century.

Others believe that Robin Hood (or Robin o' the Wood, it may
have been) was not one man but a succession of men, that the
'Master Outlaw' of the north, no matter what his true name, was
the Robin Hood of his day, until his day passed and another man
was Robin Hood after him; that it was, in fact, not a name at all
but a kind of rough title, and to think of him as one man is as
though people in a thousand years' time were to think that there
was once a man called Black-Rod, or a Lord called Chancellor in
England.

But there are yet others who believe that one man stands behind
the Robin Hood legends, as behind those of the Round Table and
that stories gathered to him as they did to Arthur. It is an awkward thing that the closer a Hero is to the hearts of the people,
the more their imagination delights to weave tales around him,
and hang on him stories rightfully belonging to other men (the
story of the harper in the enemy camp has done duty for at least
three Heroes) and the more hopelessly the real man is lost to the
people who come after him.

The first written mention of Robin comes in *Piers Ploughman*
in 1377, and turned into intelligible English, reads:

I can not say perfectly my paternoster, as the Priest it singeth,
But I can rhymes of Robin Hood and Randolf Earl of Chester.

Which clearly points to there being already more songs than one about him long established and well known, by that date.

And after that the references to him crop up from time to time. The earliest complete ballad that has come down to us is *The Lytell Geste of Robyn Hode* printed by Wynken de Worde more than a hundred years later, and it seems to have been made up from several much older ballads dove-tailed together.

It begins, oddly enough, in much the same way as some of the Round Table adventures.

Robin, in Barnsdale Forest (which was his home-hunting ground far more than Sherwood ever was) will not dine until he has a guest, and bids Little John, Will Scathelock and Much the Miller's son to walk up to the road through the forest and catch him the first-comer. No honest yeoman or poor knight or squire is to be harmed in the taking, but fat churchmen they may handle as they will and if the first-comer should be the Sheriff of Nottingham . . .

The three outlaws do as they are bidden, and return with a weary and dejected knight on his way to St Mary's Abbey at York. Robin welcomes him courteously, gives him a fine dinner, and then just as courteously asks him to pay for it before he goes.

The knight Sir Richard at Lee says that he has but ten shillings in the world, and Little John, ordered to search his saddlebags finds that he has spoken the truth.

The knight explains that his son has slain a knight of Lancashire, and to save him from the gallows, all the family lands have been mortgaged to the Abbot of St Mary. The debt has fallen due, and he has no money, and now that he is poor and has no friends to stand surety for him, he can offer no surety save Our Lady and is therefore sure to lose his lands.

But Robin, saying that he has found Our Lady to be the best surety a man could have, lends him £400, a horse and better clothes, and Little John for a squire, and Sir Richard rides on to York, where he pays off the mortgage, and then goes home to save the money for repaying Robin. At last he has scraped up the last gold piece, and has gathered, beside, a hundred bows and a hundred sheaves of arrows as a present for the outlaw who has befriended him, and with his men to carry them, sets out for Barnsdale.

On the way he tarries to watch a wrestling match and save a

73

yeoman from being murdered, and so is rather late in riding on to join Robin who is waiting for him.

Meanwhile Little John, now free of his service, has gone off to a shooting match in Nottingham. The Sheriff swears he is the finest archer ever he saw, and (happily unconscious of who he is) offers him twenty marks a year to be his servant.

Little John (one imagines him as one of those gentle and deceptively guileless-looking giants who are not quite the good natured fools they seem to be), accepts, with mental reservations about the kind of servant he is going to be, and proceeds to enjoy life hugely.

One day when the Sheriff is off hunting, he lies in bed till noon, then demands his dinner, and when the steward refuses, knocks him down. He then has a fight with the cook, who turns out to be such a splendid swordsman that they become the best of friends and decide to rob the Sheriff's treasury. This they do, and collect £300 and all the table silver, which they carry off to Robin.

Little John then sets off to find the Sheriff at his hunting, tells him that he has seen a magnificent hart and will lead him to it, and so leads him straight to the outlaws' stronghold. (John, one cannot help feeling, has had an unusually crowded day, especially when one remembers that he did not start it until noon!)

The outlaws serve their unwilling guest on his own silver, strip him of his fine clothes and give him one of their own rough tunics and make him sleep like themselves on the bare ground. Next day, on his oath never to harm Robin or any of his men in the future, they let him go.

When the time arrives for Sir Richard at Lee to pay his debt, Robin sends Little John, Much and Scathelock up to the road to look for him. They meet two black-habited Benedictine monks with a following of fifty-two men. Little John challenges them, with an arrow notched to his bowstring, and all the followers and the junior monks flee. The remaining monk they capture and bring to their leader, who as usual, entertains him to supper. Supper over, Robin asks the guest his office and the name of his Abbey, and when the monk replies that he is high Cellerer of St Mary's, greets him with joy as the Messenger of Our Lady who has sent the money she owed him. The Cellerer protests that he has never heard of the surety, and is a poor man with but twenty marks in his saddlebags. But Little John, searching them as once he searched Sir Richard's, finds £800.

Robin pouches the lot, piously remarking that he always *had* said Our Lady was the best surety in all England, and the high

74

Cellerer, now without even the price of a drink, is allowed to go on his way.

Sir Richard at Lee arrives, late because of the wrestling match, and Robin greets him with joy, and accepts the bows and arrow sheaves, but refuses the £400, and instead, gives him £400 more, explaining that Our Lady has already paid the debt twice over.

The next episode tells how the Sheriff of Nottingham offers a prize of an arrow made of gold and silver to the best archer in the north country. Robin, unable to resist such a challenge, takes seven score of his outlaws with him, the six best shots for the competition, the rest to guard against treachery. Robin himself, Gilbert of the White Hand, Little John, Much and an outlaw called Reynolds all shoot at the butts (which only seems to make five) and Robin carries off the prize. But at that instant the archers are attacked from all quarters. Little John is shot in the knee, but Robin refuses to desert him and carries him off on his back, putting him down at intervals to shoot at the pursuing Sheriff's men and then picking him up again and staggering on until they gained the shelter of the woods.

Just within the woods stands the castle of Sir Richard at Lee, who, mindful of his old debt, takes the desperate survivors in and shelters them.

The Sheriff arrives, breathing fire, and demands that Robin Hood shall be given up to him, but Sir Richard says that he will yield him up to no one save the King. The Sheriff rides off to London to the King, who swears that he will come to Nottingham within the fortnight and take both the outlaw leader and the knight, and bids the Sheriff return and gather as many good archers as possible.

While the Sheriff is gone, Robin and his men leave the castle, followed by Little John as soon as his wound is healed, and the returned Sheriff, furious to find that his birds have flown, lies in wait for Sir Richard and arrests him while he is out hawking one day.

Sir Richard's lady flees to Robin with the news, and at once the outlaw captain gathers his band and heads for Nottingham. Reaching the town, they meet the Sheriff—unfortunately for him —in the street. Robin kills him while his band drive off the men-at-arms, and they find and free Sir Richard and carry him back with them to Barnsdale and his anxiously waiting wife.

Within the fortnight, the King arrives in Nottingham, and finding Robin and Sir Richard both gone, seizes the knight's lands. He bides in Nottingham half a year and more, but though he offers Sir Richard's land to anyone who brings in word of their whereabouts, no word comes. At last a forester suggests that his only chance of finding the outlaws is to dress himself and five of his knights as monks, and trust him—the forester—to guide them to Robin's haunts. The King agrees and dressed in their dark habits, they set out.

The outlaws of course waylay them; Robin takes hold of the King's horse, bidding him bide a while, for they are poor yeomen who live by the King's deer because they have nothing else to live on, while he, a rich abbot, has churches and rent and gold, so that it was but fair that he should give them something of his charity. The King-Abbot says he has but £40 on him; Robin takes it, gives half to his men and returns the other half. The other tells him that he is the King's messenger, sent to bid Robin to come to Nottingham, and shows the royal seal in proof.

Robin says that he will come, for the King has no more loyal subjects than himself and his band, and the King's messenger must dine with him in all honour. After dinner, they hold an archery contest to entertain the guest: whoever fails to split the hazel wand to receive a buffet from his master. Twice Robin splits the wand, others follow, some failing and some winning their rose garlands, and then Robin, shooting again, misses the wand by three fingers' breadth. Gilbert reminds him of the bargain, and Robin prays the Abbot to give him his buffet. At first the seeming Abbot refuses, but when Robin will not take no for an answer, he rolls up the sleeve of his habit and gives him a blow that sends him down like a poled ox.

Amazed at the Churchman's strength, Robin picks himself up and takes a harder look into his face than he has done before, and so realises that it is the King!

Both he and Sir Richard kneel, and all the outlaws with them, and pray the King for his pardon. The King pardons them all, on condition that Robin leaves the greenwood and comes to serve him at Court.

Robin agrees, and King and outlaws return together to feast in Nottingham. Sir Richard's lands are returned to him, and Robin goes to Court to serve the King as one of the yeomen of his bed-chamber.

There he remains for 'twelve months and three', but at the end of that time all his money is spent, for the pay of the Royal Service was very small, though the honour was great, and one day he sees some young men shooting together, and remembers the days when he was the best archer in all England, and suddenly he can live the life of the Court no longer.

He asks leave of the King to visit his chapel in Barnsdale, and is given seven nights and no more. When he reaches his own hunting grounds, he sounds his horn to summon his band again, and from all over the countryside his men gather to him once more.

Two and twenty years go by, and at the end of that time Robin, who is growing old, grows also sick. He can neither eat nor drink and tells those who are still left of his men that he will go to Kirklees Priory to be let blood. He sets out with only Little John, and they ride together until they come to the crossing of a river, where an old woman is kneeling, who curses Robin Hood. He asks her why, but before she can answer, there is a sudden silence: half a page of the ballad is missing, and at the start of the next page, another woman is weeping for Robin 'that this day must he let blood'. (The story, which is otherwise so Saxon, seems here to contain an old echo of the 'Washer by the ford' who is the death omen of so many Irish and Highland Heroes.)

Robin says that the Dame Princess is his cousin and no harm will come to him in Kirklees. Arriving there, he pays her twenty pounds in gold, and she lays him on a bed and brings her bleeding knife, and opens a vein in his arm. She gives him a drug to drink so that he sleeps, and leaves him, never coming back at the proper time to stop the blood flow. Robin, waking at last, finds himself drained of almost all his life-blood, and so weak that he can scarcely move.

Nine more stanzas are missing from the MS. and when the ballad goes on again, Robin has his sword in hand and is threatening one, 'Red Roger' (now according to other versions of the story, Robin's murder is a combined effort between the Prioress and her lover, an enemy of Robin's called Roger of Doncaster) who stabs him in the side as he tries to climb through a window. In return, he strikes Roger between the neck and shoulder and leaves him lying. He knows he is dying, and Little John, who was originally left outside but seems to have now got to him, begs to be allowed to burn down the Priory, but Robin refuses, saying that he never yet harmed women and will not begin now when he is so near his death. He asks Little John to carry him out from the place, as far as the road, and at the roadside to make his grave, and bury him with his sword at his head, his bow at his side, and his arrows at his feet.

And that is the end, for the last page or pages are missing.

The story of how he shot an arrow from the window and bids Little John to bury him where it falls, is a later addition not to be found in the original ballad—unless of course it fitted somewhere, somehow, into those missing pages.

Other stories, 'Robin Hood and Guy of Gisborne', 'Robin Hood and the Potter of Wentbridge', 'Robin Hood and Alan A'Dale', 'Robin Hood and Friar Tuck' have been added over the centuries to the three ballads that make up *The Lytel Geste of Robyn Hode,* but the most vital one of all has been lost if it ever existed. And that is the story of how he first came to be an outlaw. If only there had been that one ballad more, we might have known who Robin Hood was and when he lived; as it is, there are traditions in plenty, too many, for they all contradict each other; but no ballad whose names and events might be tested against the known facts of history.

And so Robin Hood is more completely lost even than Arthur. We know the years that Arthur's campaign belong to, and the places of certain of his battles; we find him mentioned here and there by historical writers whose accounts tally too well to be complete invention. But with Robin Hood we are lost. We don't know who he was nor when he lived (we don't even know whether he should come after the Prince Llewellin in this book, or before, or maybe even as late as Owen Glyndwr). We can only feel that his place in our hearts is too sure for him to be only a cluster of invented stories, with nothing there when the inventions are stripped away.

So—assuming that behind the legend, somebody is there. . . .

The twin questions of who he was and when he was are closely knit together. The stories place him at a score of times between the twelfth and fifteenth centuries. One ballad tells how he shot at the butts before Catherine of Aragon and her ladies; for it was as though until the end of the mediaeval world and even into the beginning of the modern one, men wanted him to belong to their own generation, and tried in their tales and ballads to put him there.

One tradition makes him an Earl of Huntingdon, who fought at the Battle of Evesham with Simon de Montfort, and was outlawed for his share in de Montfort's attempt to gain a proper parliament for England. And this puts him firmly in the reign of Henry III. It was at that time also that the longbow and cloth-yard shaft which figure so largely in the stories of Robin Hood's encounters with the Sheriff of Nottingham, as they do in the history of Agincourt and Poitiers, became the regular weapon of the English yeoman, and this lends colour to the idea that he lived in the third Henry's reign.

He may have lived then, stood beside de Montfort at Evesham.

But alas! The first time that there is the faintest suggestion of his being Earl of Huntingdon is in a play written in 1601. It is in that play, too, that Maid Marion is first linked with him, though she was known a long while before that, in separate tales of her own that had nothing to do with Robin Hood at all.

Another theory is that he lived in the reign of Edward II, and that he was a follower of the Earl of Lancaster, outlawed after the Battle of Boroughbridge, and later pardoned by the King and taken for some unknown reason into the Royal Service.

Edward II whose great strength, good looks and love of disreputable company would certainly seem to fit in with the account of Robin's King in *The Little Geste*, did make a progress in the north in 1323, and for several weeks, from November 9th was in Nottingham. And documents preserved in the Exchequer containing accounts of expenses of the King's household mention a Robyn Hod several times in the following year. On November 25th he was 'discharged with 5/- as being no longer fit to work'. If this was our Robin, sickness might have made a good excuse when the call of his own forest grew too strong and he could bear the life of the Court no longer.

In the Wakefield Court Rolls for that time, according to P. Valentine Harris in his book *The Truth about Robin Hood*, is a mention of a 'Roger of Doncaster, Chaplain'. (His calling would account for his presence in Kirklees Nunnery.) A Richard at Lee finds mention as suing someone for ½ qr. of oats, the agreed price for a sheep he had sold him. A John Naylor (Little John was supposed to have been called John Naylor before he came to the forest); a Reynold; a Schacklok (Will Scarlet's name is Scadlock or Scathelock in the earlier tales and in mediaeval times Schacklok and Scadlock were interchangeable ways of spelling the same name) and a Whitehounde, which could well have been the original form of Whitehand.

It seems to add up to quite a good case. But I don't know. . . . On Valentine Harris's own showing, these were all common north country names, and probably every Manor Court Roll in four counties, over several hundred years could have produced the same collection of names at one time or another.

The theory that Robin Hood, whoever he was, belonged to the reign of Richard I has long since been almost completely discounted. There's the evidence of the longbows, to begin with, and yet I'm not sure that that proves much. Later, men retelling old tales, making them over into fresh ballads for their own day were not historians or research workers; they would naturally put into

80

their heroes' hands the weapons which they knew, and which was their especial pride, the longbow, rather than the four-foot Saxon bow that was still in use in the reigns of Richard and John. The same *could* be true of the King's name, which is given as Edward on the solitary occasion in which his name is given at all, in *The Lytel Geste*. No, the very few clues do point to his belonging to a later date. And yet oddly enough, the earlier legends have about them an atmosphere of harsher times before the mediaeval troubadours got hold of them, that seems to make them belong more naturally to the reigns of that colourful but most unsatisfactory monarch, Richard Coeur-de-Lion and his wicked and uncouth brother John. (But John could at least speak English, which was more than the Lion Heart, who looked on England as purely a milch cow to finance his crusades, ever bothered to do.) But more important than the homespun texture, the harshness of atmosphere, is the fact that these early stories seem to belong to a time when Norman and Saxon had not yet fused into one, and England had not yet come into being as she had by the reign of Edward II or even Henry III. The issue is clear-cut, not the under-privileged against the over-privileged, the poor against the rich, but quite simply, Saxon against Norman; giant-killer against giant. It is a saga in which the Hero and his champions, and the poor and dispossessed at whose side they take their stand and on whose behalf they triumph are all Saxon. Even the one knight who figures largely 'on the right side' is a Saxon. 'At Lee' is the Saxon form; if Sir Richard had been a Norman it would have been de la Lee. The unjust overlords, the cruel barons, the churchmen who wax fat on the sufferings of others, are Norman or Norman-bought to a man. Oddly enough, the one exception to this is the King himself. Richard, if Robin's King *was* Richard, early caught at popular fancy; and maybe he was the more happily remembered because he had been out of England so much, while John was conveniently on the spot to take the blame for every injustice and oppression.

Not a war of classes, then, but a war of races, and the voice of the Saxons remembering old resentments and proud of old resistance to the alien overlord, keeping alive and warm in story and ballad, the spirit of a national Hero.

Perhaps, after all, two men, or even three, have become blurred together in the hearts and heads of others coming after them, to form between them the great legend of Robin Hood. (But in any case, *no* Book of British Heroes could possibly be complete without Robin Hood.)

Chapter 7

William Wallace

THE Heroes come thick and fast, a breaking wave of Heroes, before the age of Heroes fades into the daylight of the modern world. King Edward I, who fought the wars of his young manhood against Llewellin of Wales, is not past his prime when he turns north to earn himself the title he has borne ever since: The Hammer of the Scots. And into the Prince Llewellin's place over against him steps a mere Clydesdale gentleman, William Wallace by name, who was already seven or eight when the Lord of Snowdon died.

And by and by, William Wallace is joined by Robert Bruce, the son of an ancient house with claims upon the Scottish throne, so that for a while the two march side by side through British history. But as though there cannot be two flowerings of the Herohood at the same time, Bruce remains a great man, a great leader and no more, while he shares Wallace's story, and it is only at Wallace's death, when the story becomes his own, that the Hero light passes from one man to the other.

The Bruce is incomparably the greater man, but perhaps for that very reason (or perhaps only because Wallace died young and for his Cause, and so takes his place with the young and shining men of all wars and all Peoples who never grow old, and whom Simonides sings for at Thermopilae and Wilfred Owen on the Western Front), it is Wallace for whom the light seems to burn more brightly, Wallace's spirit more than The Bruce's that twists at ones heart in the slow cadences when the Pipes play 'The Flowers of the Forest'.

William Wallace was probably born in the family home of Elderslea, probably in the same year as The Bruce, probably educated at Paisley Abbey. But it is all 'probablies'. Nobody knows for sure. Nobody knows what he looked like, but John of Fardon describes him as 'wondrously brave and bold, of goodly mien and boundless liberality'. We know that he had two brothers, Malcome and John, and both fought for the Cause of Scotland,

and John died for it on the scaffold. That is the exact sum-total of all that is known of young William Wallace, until, in his early twenties, he steps out into that place opposing King Edward I that was once Llewellin's.

How that came about is a story too long and complicated for a book of this kind. If anyone wants to know more, it can be read in the histories of Scotland and England, and read in two beautifully contradictory versions, according as to whether the writer came from north or south of the Border. (There is no such thing as completely unbiased history, and it would be cold, unreadable stuff if there were.)

But briefly this was the way of it:

In 1291, Edward quite frankly told his Privy Council that 'he had it in his mind to bring under his dominion the King and the Realm of Scotland, in the same manner that he had subdued the Kingdom of Wales', and this plan, by careful scheming and diplomacy at first, he proceeded to carry out—or try to.

The state of Scotland at the time made his task easier, for there was no King, but many claimants to the throne left vacant by the death of the little girl who was both Queen of Scots and Heiress of Norway. No strong and disinterested national leaders, no military tradition after eighty years of peace, and a nobility completely taken up with struggling for power among themselves.

And Edward was never laggard at seizing his chances.

Soon, by the brilliant use of diplomacy and cool cheek, he had got power to bestow Scotland as though it were his own fief, and contrived to get a man of his own crowned King, John Baliol, who was near to the throne in blood. Baliol was to be a puppet King, dancing when Edward pulled the strings. But eventually Edward pulled them too hard. (But perhaps he always meant to. To drive the King of Scots, his own vassal, into open revolt, would provide the perfect excuse for reducing Scotland to complete thraldom.) The puppet King revolted, and in March of 1296, Edward crossed the Tweed at Coldstream on his first Scottish campaign.

Two days later, he attacked Berwick, which was then the greatest seaport in Scotland. Baliol's garrison, under Sir William Douglas, put up a valiant defence, but the raw Fife levies were no match for Edward's troops; the town was taken and the gutters quite literally ran red. The lowest estimate of the butchered, men, women and children, was seven thousand, and the highest sixty thousand. For some hours after the town fell, the castle held out, and when it too went down, the survivors were allowed to march out with full honours of war, on taking oath never again to bear arms against England. In the Merchants' Hall of the town, which the Flemish held by a Charter binding them if need be to defend it against the English, thirty Flemish merchants, the bravest of the brave, held out until nightfall, when Edward's men fired the place, and the few who were still alive died in the flames.

That day's work changed the whole character of the war, rousing throughout Scotland a wild thirst for revenge. And in return for Berwick, Redesdale and Tynedale were desolated by and by, and Corbridge, Carlisle, Lanercost and Hexham went up in flames.

But for the moment, the triumph was Edward's. Dunbar Castle fell to him and three earls and seventy knights, the chief leaders in the land, were captured and sent to English prisons. To the shores of the Moray Firth and back again, Edward marched his troops in the blustery spring weather, planting garrisons in town and castle as he went, and receiving the forced homage of the people. He picked Baliol off his throne and tossed him into England after the Dunbar leaders, and the Coronation Stone with him, hoping that without this sacred object, the Scots would more readily forget old freedoms and old pride. He held his Parliament at Berwick at the end of August, set Englishmen in all the highest offices of State, and arranged to bring in the English Judicial System. Six months after he crossed the Border he marched south again, with a full summer's work behind him.

By now he had a French war on his hands, and little time to worry about Scotland further. He must have thought that the country would bide quiet enough for a while anyway, licking its wounds. But in truth, the mutterings of the next revolt had broken out the moment he was across the border, and by April, Aberdeen was up in arms. Attacks were launched against the English garrisons in Galloway, a full-scale rising broke out in Moray which was destined to spread through the whole north.

And now, as John Fordun says, '*William Wallace in Clydesdale lifted up his head.*'

He was already in command of a company of irregular troops, and will hardly have been sitting quiet at home, while Scotland went roaring up about his ears. But this is the first we really hear of him; how with his band he carried out a surprise raid on the English garrison at Lanark, and slew the English Sheriff of the town, William de Hazelrigg. Hazelrigg's death was a shock to the morale of the English garrisons in the south-west, and put fresh heart into the Scots. And during the weeks that followed, there

84

gathered to Wallace many men of fierce courage and bitter heart, and his war bands grew and grew. Soon he was the accepted chief of the desperate bands that kept up in the south-west of Scotland a war of raids and harryings and convoy ambushes against the English forces. It was the same in the north and north-east; but as yet, none of the nobles had joined these small valiant bands; it was a revolt of farmers and ordinary clansmen led by country gentlemen such as William Wallace and Andrew de Moray, young son of one of the Dunbar captives.

But the time had come for the scattered resistance to be drawn together into a national movement. And the first man to emerge as leader of this combined revolt was Sir William Douglas, who had sworn fealty to the English King after his capture at Berwick, and renounced his extorted homage the moment he was free again among his own hills. Now, with a hastily gathered band, he joined Wallace at Perth, and together they marched on Scone, where Edward's Justiciar now held court. The Justiciar was the central symbol of Edward's iron grip on Scotland, and to overthrow him would be in a way to overthrow Edward's rule. But the Justiciar, getting wind of their coming, escaped, leaving however, a good supply of booty behind him to help fill the Scottish war-chest.

All those risings were nominally in the cause of Baliol, actually in the cause of Scotland.

The King, too busy with France to come himself, sent orders for the instant and utter crushing of the uprising, and at the same time he confiscated all Douglas's English lands. (Many of the nobles, including the Bruce himself, held lands on both sides of the Border, and were both Scottish chiefs and Norman barons.) And on June 14th, the Earl of Surrey, the victor of Dunbar, crossed the Border with a powerful force levied from all the northern counties.

Meanwhile, Wallace and his bands were scouring the country between Forth and Tay, turning out the newly planted English clergy, and putting to the sword all the English troops they met. Meanwhile also, Bishop Wishart of Glasgow had gathered together a federation of war leaders, among them Sir John Stewart of Bonhill, Sir Alexander de Lindsay, Sir Richard de Lundin, and most unexpectedly (the reason shall be told in another place) Robert the Bruce, the young Earl of Carrick. The federation, however, was too full of warring parties and old clan jealousies to be a success, and when Scots and English met at Irvine, the bad blood among the Scots leaders made resistance hopeless. There was no battle, and on July 9th, the leaders, including the Bruce, capitulated to 'Our Lord Messire Edward, by the Grace of God King of England, Lord of Ireland and Duke of Guyenne.'

This looked like the end of the rising. It was no such thing. Wallace and young Moray were still on the warpath, Moray harrying the English garrisons of the north-east, capturing Aberdeen and burning the ships in the harbour, while Wallace was besieging Dundee.

These two must be dealt with. A second English Army was sent north, joined with the first, and under Surrey's command advanced on the Forth. It was harvest-time, but no harvest was gathered in the Lowlands that year. Wallace raised the Siege of Dundee, one of the last English strongholds left north of the Forth, and marched to meet them.

Stirling, with its one bridge over the deep tidal waters of the Forth, was the gateway between the two parts of Scotland, and this was for Wallace the one and obvious place to hold the enemy; but even with Moray's victorious force added to his, the two young leaders knew themselves desperately outnumbered. Also the English Army contained a strong body of heavily armed knights, while Wallace had the merest handful, and the hard core of the English Army were well-armed veterans of the wars in France and Palestine. Above all, they had a tradition of victory over the Scots. The Scots, on the other hand, had little experience of any save guerrilla warfare and the twelve-foot spear was almost their only weapon. The one asset they had was supreme confidence in their leaders.

Wallace reached the Forth first, and placed his men where the road from the south and Stirling Bridge, after crossing the marshy river levels, rose sharply to strike into the hills. Here they would have hazel woods for cover, while the English would have to advance across open ground to come at them. The English encamped on the further bank, and on the morning of September 11th, Surrey sent a couple of friars across, to try to negotiate a surrender on terms. To them, Wallace said, 'Tell your people that we have not come here to gain peace, but are prepared for battle, to avenge and deliver our country. Let them come up when they like, and they will find us ready to meet them to their beards.'

There was more than defiance in this answer, for by indicating that the Scots intended to wait where they were on their own side of the river until attacked, Wallace hoped to draw the English Army into the position he wanted. His hope was justified. Surrey belonged to the old school of warfare, whose only idea was frontal

attack, and a frontal attack he promptly ordered, heedless of the advice of his officers.

The plan was suicidal; the bridge was not wide enough for more than two horsemen abreast, but nevertheless, the order was given and the vanguard began to cross. The crossing went on for hours, and all the while Wallace held his little army like hounds in leash, still and silent among the steep woods. He waited until the enemy vanguard had deployed on the level ground to cover the crossing of the main body. Still he waited, watching the dark files below him, the mailed knights on their destriers, the well-trained spears and the Welsh longbow men, the hated leopards of England on the wind-rippled banners over all. If he attacked too soon, he would have an easy victory, but the English losses would be slight; if he waited too long, the army on the river levels would be too strong for his wild hillmen. He waited until exactly as many men had crossed as he felt he had a reasonable chance of overcoming, and then—it was about eleven in the morning—he set his horn to his lips and sounded the charge.

The whole Scottish battle line swept down from the woods, and while the centre and left wing flung themselves straight upon the English lines, the right wing, composed of spearmen, charged past the English left as though to drive in a flanking attack, and not until too late did the English, facing about to meet it, realise its true purpose, to seize and hold the bridge, cutting them off from reinforcements or retreat.

Panic swept through the English ranks, and the Scots jammed them down into the loop of the river, which was twenty feet deep just there, with a strong current, and the tide was rising. A few knights, rallied by Sir Marmaduke de Twenge who had led the vanguard, fought their way back before the bridge timbers gave under the blows of Scottish axes. But the Scots and the river settled with the rest, and there was nothing that the Earl of Surrey could do about it, while at sight of the slaughter the panic spread from the north bank to the south, and his men broke and streamed back without a blow being struck.

The Lowlands were clear of English troops, save for the flying stragglers from Stirling Bridge with the Scots, who of course knew the river fords, hard upon their heels. Scotland rang like a bell with news of the victory, but there had been a price to pay. The Scottish losses were not heavy, but young Moray was mortally wounded, and died a few weeks later.

From Stirling Bridge, Wallace turned back to finish taking Dundee. Then, wildly heartened by their victory, his army sacked

Berwick and swept south across the border, racing through Cumberland and Northumberland before turning north again in mid-December. Hexham Priory was only saved by the intervention of Wallace himself, and 'The Scots are coming!' had become a signal for people to drive off their cattle into the most inaccessible places they could think of.

Wallace had recovered the lost castles of Scotland and driven the invaders beyond her frontiers. Unaided by the powerful nobles of the country, he had broken, in this one direction, the power of the mighty Edward. And now, in the lack of any ordered government, and with the leadership fallen on him, he took the title of 'Guardian of Scotland on behalf of King John'. ✕

It was too late in the year for another English attack, but Edward and his Government were already making preparations for the spring. Three thousand troops were raised; the whole feudal levy of England. Wallace drew back from the Border, and that winter was busy organising his resistance. That winter also, he received knighthood 'At the hands of a certain distinguished Earl of the Scottish Nation' and it seems quite possible that this was the young Earl of Carrick, Robert the Bruce, who had long since 'Come out' again for the Scottish Resistance. If so, there is a fitness in the thing that suits the pattern of a Hero-tale.

By mid-February the fight was on again and the Earl of Surrey was in Roxburgh, but it was not until the end of the French war in June, that the King himself was free to come north and meanwhile Wallace had burned the towns of Roxburgh and Haddington, in an early form of 'scorched earth' warfare.

Edward crossed the Tweed at Coldstream, and marched on Edinburgh, slowed up by the usual heavy baggage train, by the Scot's scorched earth policy, and by Wallace's delaying tactics in general. Among the very few nobles who had joined Wallace by that time were Robert the Bruce and John Comyn, Baliol's nephew, who was later to die by the Bruce's dagger, as will be told in another place. They held off from pitched battle as long as they could, seeking to starve the English out, but a July day came when Scots and English faced each other again, drawn up on Slamannan Moor, south of Falkirk.

Once again Wallace was face to face with a War Host enormously larger than his own and this time it was commanded not by old hide-bound Surrey but by the King himself, the most brilliant general of his time. Face to face also with a weapon that the Scots had not confronted in strength before, the longbow, and in the end it was the longbow that settled the issue.

Wallace had drawn up his troops on high ground fronting a stretch of marsh in a strong defensive position, with his handful of cavalry in the rear, so that he might be able to throw them in as a final blow when the enemy was at breaking-point. His infantry, since they would have to face cavalry attack, were drawn up in four Schiltroons—circular clumps, each consisting of two ranks of spearmen, the outer rank kneeling, with their long spears pointing outwards. His few archers, shortbow men from Ettrick Forest, were on the flanks and between the Schiltroons. The whole battle formation has been criticised often enough since, but in actual fact is identical with that which won Waterloo, the chief difference being that the French artillery fire was not so close and deadly as the English archery of five hundred years earlier.

Edward formed in the orthodox three divisions. Norfolk and Hereford commanded the Right, the fighting Bishop of Durham the Left, and he himself took the Centre. At first it went well for the Scots; the English Right charged and became bogged. The Left, forewarned, got round the quagmire, followed by the King, and halted while the Right drew back and reformed, the flights of short arrows having little effect on the heavily armed knights. Then both battle-wings charged together. The Scots archers were ridden down, the handful of cavalry broke and fled. But the Schiltroons held as firm as rocks. The successive thundering charges broke like waves against them and were flung back in confusion, until, seeing how it went, Edward halted his Centre, which had not yet become engaged, and ordered up his longbow men to shoot across the Marsh. The Schiltroons were a sitting target; there was no cover, and their very strength and rigidity prevented them being quickly reformed and moved forward into a charge. A few horsemen surrounding Wallace remained with the Schiltroons. If all his cavalry had stayed at their posts and he had been able to use them to break up the longbow men, he might yet have turned the tide. But the cavalry had broken and been swept away. The bowmen focused their fire on to small sections of the Schiltroons until they tore gaps in them, and then held their fire while the cavalry charged in.

The broken Schiltroons were swept away, the long spears, so deadly in formation, were almost useless once the formation was broken. The battle became a rout and the rout a massacre, as the heavily armoured knights rode down the half-armed tribesmen.

A full third of the Scots troops fell that day. Wallace by super-human strength and valour, managed to rally the rest and bring them off, but many of those were drowned in the crossing of the muddy-banked tidal Carron.

Wallace's army was the main effective force of the Scots, and once it was dispersed there could be little more active resistance. Edward seized Stirling (as much of it as had escaped Wallace's scorched earth policy) and marched on into Carrick to meet the supply fleet coming up the Clyde, and was back in Carlisle by September.

Falkirk was a worse blow to Scotland than Dunbar had been. The loss of men was greater, and it came at the end of a time of triumph and rising hope. And Wallace left on Slamannan Moor, not only the flower of his army, but his own reputation as a leader. The fact that Falkirk was the only defeat of the whole campaign made no difference. He had still seven years to live, but his end began that day.

And yet maybe the English triumph did not seem so great to Edward. He had cut to pieces the most formidable army of Scotland, but his actual gains amounted only to this: that he had managed to remain north of the Border for just over two months; he had marched through the Lowlands with a starving and half-mutinous army and failed to get beyond the Tay. He had re-taken, rebuilt and re-garrisoned Stirling, but had to leave it so unsupported that within six months it had fallen to the Scots again. And he had left Sir William Wallace and the Earl of Carrick still alive and active.

Wallace continued to fight for Scotland in one way or another, through the rest of his life. But now he was no more than a leader of guerrillas as he had been at the very first, and without the hope that he had had then. The jealous nobles were on him like a pack of wolves. But they could not strip him of his position as Guardian of Scotland; he laid it down promptly and with dignity, of his own accord. By the end of December the Earl of Carrick and John Comyn, Comyn the Red, were joint Guardians in his place, an unlikely team, when one remembers that they represented rival claims to the Crown. But perhaps Wallace's example had begun to work on even some of the nobles, so that at least for a while they could sink their personal feuds and power-struggles for the good of Scotland. It is certainly about then, that many of them began to come out clearly for the first time on the side of the Resistance.

Border war continued throughout the following summer, and Wallace played an active part in it, but in August it was decided that he should go to France (negotiations between France and

Scotland had been going on for some time) to try for help from King Philip.

He went, and was well received and given promises of help, though nothing much ever came of them; given also, Philip's official recommendation to the Pope, together with letters of safe-conduct for the journey to Rome. To Rome he went, and pleaded his cause, or rather Scotland's, before the Holy Father. The outcome was a sharp protest and reproof to the English King from Pope Boniface VIII. But Edward, the Hammer of the Scots, was not one to care over much for protests and reproofs. It was to all intents and purposes a wasted journey.

For four years, with the suddenness with which he first enters history, William Wallace drops out of it again. But the two or three casual references to him that exist, seem to show that he was still the guerrilla leader, the captain of small bands of irregular troops, keeping alive the flame of the Resistance he had done so much to kindle. It is to these lost years when history has nothing to say of William Wallace that many of the legends of him belong; a host of stories such as the one told in the ballad of 'Gude Wallace'.

> *Would ye hear of William Wallace,*
> *And sek him as he goes,*
> *Into the Lan' of Lanark,*
> *Amang his mortal foes?*
>
> *There was fyften English sogers*
> *Unto his ladie cam,*
> *Said, 'Gie us William Wallace,*
> *That we may have him slain.'*
>
> *Would ye gie William Wallace,*
> *That we may have him slain,*
> *And ye's be wedded to a lord,*
> *The best in Christendom.*

The bribe is too tempting and the Ladie tells the soldiers that Wallace will come to her bower door that very night at seven. But when he comes, her heart fails her, and she tells him what she has done, and that the house is surrounded by soldiers. Wallace wastes no time in being angry, he simply asks for her gown and petticoat, and putting them on, with her broadest belt with a silver clasp to bind about his middle, he takes a pitcher in either hand and sets out, like a girl going to the well. The English soldiers are completely taken in, but four 'brave Southrons' chase him none the less, thinking maybe that a bit of fun with a girl will enliven the time while they wait for William Wallace to come out. Wallace flings aside the pitchers and draws his trusty brand— presumably he has it belted on under his skirts—and slays them pair by pair, then, as he so often did in real life, and as The Bruce would soon be doing after him, he heads for the hills. Presently he comes upon a girl washing her clothes, and asks her for news.

> 'What news, what news, ye well-far'd may?
> What news hae ye to gie!'
> 'Ill news, ill news', the fair may said,
> 'Ill news I hae to thee.
>
> 'There's fyften English sogers
> Into that thatched inn,
> Seeking Sir William Wallace,
> I fear that he is slain.'
>
> 'Have ye money in your pocket?
> Pray lend it unto me,
> And when I come this way again,
> Repaid ye weal shall be.'
>
> She's put her hand in her pocket,
> And taen out shillings three:
> He turned him right and round about,
> And thankd the weel-far'd may.
>
> He had not gone a long rig length,
> A rig length and a span,
> Until he met a bold begger,
> As sturdy as could gang.
>
> 'What news, what news, ye bold begger?
> What news hae ye to gie?'
> 'Oh heavy news', the begger said,
> 'I hae to tell to thee.
>
> 'There's fyften English sogers,
> I fear the chief is slain.'
> I heard them in yon inn
> Vowing to kill him Wallace,

> *'Will ye change apparell wi' me, auld man?*
> *Change your apparell for mine?*
> *And when I come this way again,*
> *Ye'll be my ain poor man.'*

Clad in the beggar's clothes, William Wallace goes down to the inn, where the English sogers are still drinking. They ask him for news, and promise him money if he can tell them where William Wallace is.

The beggar is delighted to oblige.

> *Tell down, tell down your good red gold*
> *Upon this table head,*
> *And ye' shall William Wallace see,*
> *Wi' the down-come of Robin Hood.*

But no sooner have they put the money down, than he flings the candles to the floor, and again draws his trusty brand and in the darkness and confusion kills them every one. After which he sits down at the table head and calls for more wine.

The ending of the story has a beautiful simplicity which thinks of everything, even the fact that as the Hero cannot very well go back to his old love, he will be needing a new one.

> *'Now if there be a Scotsman here,*
> *He'll come and drink wi' me;*
> *But if there be an Englishman*
> *It is his time to flee.'*

> *The Goodman was an Englishman,*
> *And to the hills he ran;*
> *The Goodwife was a Scots woman,*
> *And she came to his hand.*

John Comyn and the rest had been beaten by hammer blow after hammer blow into a state of hopeless acquiescence; The Bruce in 1302, and the others in 1304 submitted and received sentences of banishment. Only Wallace, suddenly, standing clear again from those four shadow-years, refused to accept the King's peace.

'I say that if all the people of Scotland yield obedience to the King of England, or depart each one from his own freedom, I and my companions who are willing to cleave to me in this matter will stand for the liberty of the Kingdom, and if God aid us, we will obey no man save the King or his Lieutenant'. . . . But indeed the King's peace would not have been for him, even if he had most humbly sought it. For Edward's feeling towards him seems to have been quite different from his feeling towards the other Scottish leaders. There was something personal in it; a deadly hate between the two men, which nothing save the death of one of them could end, and so for Wallace, there were to be no terms save complete and unconditional surrender.

Events crowd thick and fast now. Early in March Wallace was defeated in a skirmish in Tweeddale, the English having tracked him down by the help of a certain John of Musselburgh, who got ten shillings from the King's own hand for his reward. He escaped, and brought off the few men left to him, but it was his last fight. Now he was the only leader outside the half ruins of Stirling Castle, who still upheld the Resistance; and in July, Stirling Castle fell after a magnificent resistance of many months, and Wallace was quite alone, with no more than a hundred at most of loyal spears at his back.

Now, Edward was Master of all Scotland, and yet he knew that he would never be truly Master while one landless knight with a handful of tattered clansmen still loyal to him, and an inability to understand when he was beaten, continued free in the hills to gather an army again. It roused all the leopard in old Edward, and he spared no pains to hunt him down, even offering to remit the ransoms and ease the banishment sentences of Sir John Comyn and several other of the nobles, if they should 'take pains between now and twenty days after Christmas, to capture Messire William le Waleys and to give him up to our Lord the King'. And The Bruce was later officially thanked for his own efforts in the same direction. But there 'is no proof that any of them did anything but look for him in the places where they knew he was not', and the fact remains that none of them took him.

That final treachery was left to Sir John de Menteith, Governor of Dumbarton, and once a fighter for Scotland's Cause; and did not come for another year and a half.

Wallace was betrayed in the house of a certain Ralf Rae, who had been one of the Stirling Garrison and was released on condition of securing him; and taken as he lay sleeping, by Menteith, who later received a hundred and fifty-one pounds for the job, rather better pay than Judas Iscariot's thirty pieces of silver.

Sir William Wallace might have had his throat slit there and then, for the mere moss-trooping brigand that the English claimed him to be. But such a quick death would have been too merciful for the man who had defied the King of England and held him in play for more than eight years. They marched him down through England in the dust of high summer. They marched him into London on August 22nd and brought him before the King. There is no record of what passed between them, but one wonders if Edward turned away from William Wallace as, three hundred years later, the Marquis of Argyll turned from the level gaze of the captive Montrose.

He was handed over to the Civil Authorities, and tried for treason in Westminster Hall. (Alone of all the Resistance leaders now having their lands restored to them, he had never sworn any oath of allegiance to the English King; and therefore he was the one of them all who could not by any possibility be guilty of that particular charge!) But his death was already determined upon, and so any charge would serve. He was put through the form of a trial. He said only one thing in his own defence: it was all there was to say.

'I was never a traitor.'

He was sentenced to be hanged, drawn and quartered, and the sentence was carried out the same day. They dragged him through the streets chained on a horse-drawn hurdle, to Smithfield Market, and there the sentence was carried out. He was hanged on a gallows built especially high so that everyone in the crowd should have a good view, and cut down with the breath still in him, for the rest of the sentence to be carried out.

We are so used to reading 'Hanged, drawn and quartered' in our history books that it has taken on the cheap ring of a catchphrase, and we seldom stop to think what it really means. Many of us do not even know, for parts of the sentence are so foul that they are seldom set down in a book at all. It was the last sickening torture and degredation that men could think of, to inflict on the body of another man.

When the red butcher's work was done, the quarters of William Wallace's body were sent to three cities of Scotland and one of northern England, for a dumb warning. His sword arm was hung on the bridge at Newcastle, over the town drain; his head, mounted on a spear, but lacking the ivy crown, was set up on London Bridge.

Seven years before, he had stood to defend Stirling Bridge; seven months later, Robert the Bruce was crowned King of Scots, at Scone.

Chapter 8

Robert the Bruce

WE must go back, back again to the beginning of the story shared by William Wallace and Robert the Bruce.

In September of 1286, a few months after the death of King Alexander III certain nobles of Scotland gathered together at Turnberry Castle on the coast of Carrick, and misliking the idea of a regency, decided to refuse his little daughter, Margaret of Norway for their Queen. In her stead they chose one of their own number, a cousin of the late King's, Robert Bruce, old Lord of Annandale, who Alexander had named as his heir before he had a child of his own to take the crown after him. Old Bruce was old indeed, but he had two sons and a fine big brood of grandsons, and among those grandsons, eldest son of *his* eldest son and a mother who came of the old Royal Celtic stock and was Countess of Carrick in her own right, was the Robert of this story.

Young Robert was twelve at the time, and will have been there among the other pages in the great hall of Turnberry Castle, his home, to see his grandfather chosen King of Scotland, and one can imagine the pride and excitement swelling in his chest and making the torches seem to burn brighter.

But nothing much ever came of this King-choosing. There was some kind of armed rising against little Princess Margaret's Regents, with a few castles taken; but it fizzled out, and no one was ever punished. And when, three years later, Edward I of England arranged with the Scottish Regents for his young son to marry their Princess, neither the Bruces nor their following made any move against the marriage. England and most of Scotland had been good friends for many years; they accepted the plan happily enough on both sides of the Border, and it looked like being a way out of many difficulties.

Alas! The little seven-year-old Queen, sent from Norway for her wedding, died in Orkney, some said from the effects of sea-sickness, some said from poison.

After that, the desire for a King on the Scottish throne flared up again. Eleven men put forward their claims. Seven were bastards and so were virtually ruled out at once; and of the remaining four, one was old Robert Bruce, and another John Baliol, Lord of Galloway. Another—outside, as it were, the main stream—was Black William Comyn of Baddenoch, who based his claim on descent from an earlier King, Donald Bàn. To avoid a bloody civil war, all these men agreed to turn to an outsider to arbitrate, and if the Pope were ruled out—the Holy Father of that time was known to be thoroughly corrupt—the obvious choice was Edward of England. Many of the Scottish Lords holding land both sides of the Border were already his liege men for English estates. He had Scottish blood in his veins, and through his son, had all but married into Scotland anyway, so to Edward they turned. And Edward, having got himself declared Liege Lord of Scotland (as has been told in the last story) found for John Baliol, whom he knew was his puppet and would dance to his tune, and against the Bruces, who would always remain their own men.

On November 19th, 1292, John Baliol did homage for his Scots Kingdom to Edward of England.

Old Bruce retired from the game after that, making over his place as head of the family to his son; and his son, either from patriotism or simply because he did not care, made no move to raise trouble. Only he would not do homage to Baliol for his Scots lands, and got over the difficulty by making them over to *his* son, young Robert.

So Robert, still only a boy, was now Earl of Carrick, and did his homage at Stirling; but save for that, we know no more of him for nearly two years, while Edward was twisting Baliol's tail, goading the worm to turn by every means in his power, that he might have an excuse for stamping on him. At the end of that time, the worm duly turned, and with a committee of twelve nobles made a treaty with France, for a combined invasion of England. Edward got wind of it, and seized all the English estates both of Baliol himself and the nobles. Baliol countered by confiscating the Scottish estates of all his nobles who had lands in England. This must have come at a particularly awkward time for young Bruce, for we get word of him again just then, and the word is that he is getting married—to Isobel, daughter of the Earl of Mar and granddaughter of Llewellin of Wales, and it cannot have been a good moment to be losing his estates from both sides at once.

Baliol denounced his fealty, and Edward declared Baliol deposed and summoned him to give an account of himself. Baliol refused. Edward quoted Holy Writ: 'Be it unto the fool according to his folly' and gave the order for war. Preparations began on both sides of the Border and continued all winter, and with the spring the hundred years peace went roaring up in flames. ✕

Edward marched north. Young Carrick, along with the other nobles deposed by Baliol, did their homage to him in his camp at Wark, and a few days later he crossed the Tweed at Coldstream, and attacked Berwick, and having taken the place, made a red massacre there that was not forgotten in Scotland for many a long year.

The story of that summer in Scotland has been told in the last chapter. It has been told how the land that Edward had supposed crushed rose again in the following spring, and how 'William Wallace in Clydesdale lifted up his head'. But it has been left to this chapter to tell how Robert the Bruce changed his allegiance and joined Bishop Wishart's federation of Scottish war leaders.

Surrey, who led the King's Army north that spring to crush the new rising, sent young Bruce ahead to harry the lands of Sir William Douglas (the same Sir William Douglas who swore a forced fealty after Berwick and then repudiated it). Bruce carried out his orders, even capturing Lady Douglas and her children. But the task apparently turned his stomach and gave him furiously to think. He released his captives, denounced his fealty to Edward, and came out into revolt with the Scottish nobles.

The federation was undermined from the first by old Clan jealousies, and when Scots and English met at Irvine the bad blood dividing the Scottish leaders made resistance hopeless. There was no battle, and on July 9th, the leaders, including Bruce, capitulated to 'Our Lord Messire Edward, by the Grace of God King of England, Lord of Ireland and Duke of Guyenne'.

This looked like the end of the rising, but Wallace and Moray were still at large and deadly dangerous. To deal with them, another army was sent north, only to be broken and hurled back by the two young leaders, at Stirling Bridge, and the Scots in their turn swept over the Border to avenge Berwick a hundredfold on the north of England.

Bruce, finding that the Resistance was not finished after all, was 'out' again by November and that month, with Edward's Government already preparing for a great thrust in the spring, and William Wallace calling back his own troops over the border, to make ready to receive it, it seems likely that the stories of the two heroes actually touch for the first time, with the Clydesdale gentleman receiving knighthood at the young Earl of Carrick's hands.

Spring came and the war was in full blaze again, and in July came the tragic defeat of Falkirk, that lost to Scotland all that had been gained. The Bruce was one of the little knot of cavalry that were broken and driven from the field that day.

Wallace resigned his Guardianship of the realm, and within a few months The Bruce, and John Comyn, son to Black William Comyn had been appointed to share the Guardianship between them. They retained that position while Wallace was no more than a guerrilla leader, until, hammered into hopelessness, first Bruce and then the rest of the nobles submitted to the English King and received sentences of banishment. And only William Wallace was left to carry on the struggle to the bitter end on a scaffold in Smithfield Market.

According to one story, Robert the Bruce was present at that trial and execution, and both those who believe the story and those who hotly deny it, seem to think of it as some frightful and appalling piece of treachery. But of course, since he had renewed his allegiance to Edward it is not treachery to Scotland, not in the legal sense. And in the true sense, to the mediaeval mind, and even much later, there is no treachery in going to see a friend executed (when Sir Walter Raleigh was beheaded, close on three hundred years later, Old Palace Yard was packed with admirers come to pay him their last respects, friends who had come to be with him at the end). But whether he was actually present or not, Wallace's death, showing him that he had come to the place where there could be no more changing to and fro, made a complete change in the young Earl of Carrick. He ceased in that moment to be merely a good soldier and a sensible man who knew when he was beaten. It is as though, standing in the stink of Smithfield Market on that sweating August day, he reached out to receive from the man on the scaffold, the sword of Scotland's freedom, and with the sword, which he never laid down until that freedom was won, the Hero-light passed from one man to another.

Back in Scotland, and feeling perhaps that he was not strong enough to handle the fight alone, The Bruce made some kind of pact with Red John Comyn. No one knows the details, nor does anyone know what possessed Comyn to betray the pact to Edward —it is not even certain that he did, but *someone* did, and The Bruce believed that it was Comyn. Furious for a showdown, he summoned the other to meet him on February 10th at the Kirk of the Franciscans at Dumfries, and there they met before the High Altar. And again, no one knows quite what happened. The Bruce accused him of his betrayal. They were both hot-blooded men and they forgot where they were. The quarrel, fed with all the bitterness of old rivalries long suppressed flared up between them. Daggers were out, and both struck together—and on the Chancel floor, Red John Comyn lay dead.

The actual killing was not the most important part of what had happened; it was horribly unfortunate, for it meant a blood-feud with one of the most powerful houses in Scotland; but to kill, in the hot blood of a quarrel, though regrettable, was not a thing that seemed too serious to most men. But the place was quite another matter. To kill in God's House and before the High Altar at that was the most appalling sacrilege. Bruce knew that it must cost him the support of the Church, which he had had until now; it must add to the number of his enemies and strip him of some of his strongest friends. But the thing was done, beyond calling back, and all he could do now was to act quickly, before the feeling of men had time to harden against him.

He rode north through the night and the February rain to Bishop Wishart, one of the few Churchmen whom he felt would still stand by him. The Bishop was waiting for him and brought out from his treasury the old forbidden standard of the Kings of Scotland, the Lion and the Scarlet lilies. He gave The Bruce absolution for Comyn's death, and when a goldsmith had hurriedly made a gold circlet, rode with him to Scone.

The Coronation was on Palm Sunday, 1306; the palm branches and veiled crosses and the violet colour of mourning were a strange background for such a ceremony, and many of the men gathered there were to die for that day's work. The Abbot performed the ceremony, with Bishop Lampton and staunch old Wishart, Bishop of Moray, uncle to young Moray so long dead at Stirling Bridge. Bruce's own brothers and kinsman stood about him, one English knight, Christopher Seton who was husband to his sister Christina, and his closest friend, Sir James Douglas, son of old Sir William Douglas. These, and many other of the nobles. The Earl of Fife, who should by hereditary right have set the Crown on the King's head was only a young boy, and in London at that, but his sister Lady Buchan (and she the wife of another John Comyn!) calmly took her husband's horses and rode to Scone to play her brother's part.

So Robert the Bruce was crowned King of Scots. King of a country whose castles were all in the hands of the enemy, whose trade and agriculture were in ruins. His Lowlands were flooded with English to seven or eight times the full strength of the Scottish Army, and he had a blood-feud on his hands, so huge that it could almost be counted as civil war. It seemed a lunatic venture, and even his young wife cried out in protest against it. 'Alas! We are but King and Queen of the May!'

By rights, he should have gone under in six weeks. In fact, he remained in the field for well over twenty years, and at the end of them, Scotland was free, and joined England at last only when a Scottish King (admittedly a very unworthy one) came to rule over both countries.

The Crowning over, Bruce set about gathering men to his standard. While in London, Edward had two live swans with gold chains round their necks brought into his banqueting hall, and all his knights took oath upon them never to sheathe their swords until Scotland was crushed. Afterwards, he graciously distributed the lands of Bruce and his followers, in advance, among those present.

Three months later, the Battle of Methven ended in an English victory. Bishop Wishart was captured and imprisoned; sixteen knights were hanged at Newcastle, without trial. Yet again, the whole cause seemed lost. But Bruce, with what men he could gather, was away to Athol to raise more.

After that, one can guess at wanderings much like those of Bonnie Prince Charlie and to this time belongs the legend of the spider. The Bruce is heard of here and there, among the Islands of Kintyre and the Hebrides; there is word of a foray in one place, a skirmish with English troops in another. The Scottish King had taken to the heather, and the heather hides him from our eyes almost as well as it did from the eyes of the English troops; until in February of 1307, he was in Arran, in sight of his own Carrick shores. And with him still was Sir James Douglas, who had long since proved his worth, not only as a friend and fighting-man, but as a poacher when times were hard, and an inspired inventor of ways to put strange fears into the enemy. (One might say today, that he was an expert in psychological warfare.) Spring was at hand, and soon Edward's War Hosts would be on the move again; and Bruce knew that the time had come to be taking a more active hand once more.

He sent a man across the Firth to scout around, and if and when the time seemed ripe for a fresh rising, to light a fire on Turnberry Head. Night after night they watched the shore, and night after night all remained dark along the Carrick coast; and then one night at last they saw the long-awaited signal! The fire burned clear on Turnberry Head, and they took to the boats that had been waiting for the crossing. . . . And the fire was no signal beacon after all, but only a dry grass fire such as springs up sometimes before the spring rain.

The news that the horrified scout had for them when they landed was enough to sicken the strongest heart.

Carrick was swarming with the English; they even held Turnberry itself with a strong garrison and his Queen and little daughter, two sisters and even Lady Buchan, who had crowned him, were all in English hands. They had been taken from sanctuary by the Earl of Ross, who had come down on the English side, and his wife and little Marjorie and Lady Buchan were all penned like wild beasts in wooden cages on the ramparts of Roxburgh Castle, or the Tower. His friends and two of his surviving brothers, the youngest Neil, little more than a boy, had suffered the same hideous death as William Wallace, in Berwick town.

Hope had sunk so low that even some of his staunchest supporters had given up the struggle and made terms with Edward. It was all over. Finished. And there were those who said to Bruce 'Get away!—Quickly! Back to Arran! Norway will give you shelter——".

But The Bruce chose to stay, and there were a loyal handful still, James Douglas among them, who chose to stay with him. If the men of his own countryside were beyond power to help him, the land itself, that he had known since first his legs were long enough to carry him beyond the gate of Turnberry Castle, was still his friend; and for the moment he simply melted into the landscape, while Douglas—that tall black-haired, olive-skinned daredevil, with a gentle charm of manner and a lisp to his speech that men remembered after once meeting him, went off to see if there was anything to be done in Douglasdale. He found the English there as in Carrick, but found also a valiant few of his clansmen to join him in secret, and on Palm Sunday, when the English garrison of Douglas Castle, over sure of their security, were in church, they surrounded the Kirk, and when all was ready, raised the Douglas war cry and attacked. When they had made an end there, they went up to the castle, dealt with the few men left on duty, and did full justice to the Sunday dinner that was making ready in the kitchen. Then, since they were far too few to hold the place, they took whatever was of use to them of weapons and gear, broached the food casks, fouled the wells by tipping a few dead bodies down them, and set fire to any part of the buildings that would burn. Then they departed, having made one of the strongest holds in the country unfit for further use.

Word of the sacking of Douglas Keep spread through the country, lifting the hearts of the Scots and causing the English to look uneasily over their shoulders; and in the days that followed, more and more men came in to join their King in the heather, so that within a couple of months he had enough fighters at his back not only to beat off a sizeable English force when they did come to grips with him at last, but even to besiege Ayr for a few days, though he had to raise the siege at the first sign of a relief force being on the way.

It seemed that Scottish affairs were on the upward swing again. But even so, there is no saying how matters would have ended, with a new and stronger English War Host already on the march north. But on June 7th at Burgh-on-Sands, within sight of Scotland, the old Hammer of the Scots died.

He had left orders that if he should die on this new and greatest Scottish campaign, his bones were to be carried on at the head of the Army. But the second Edward was not the man the first Edward had been, and only too glad of the excuse, he turned again to escort the old King's body south and bury it with all pomp and circumstance, at Westminster.

The unexpected respite gave The Bruce a chance to deal with the civil war he still had on his hands, and leaving Douglas on the Border to keep the English happy, he rode northward against Buchan and the other Comyn and Baliol men. He dealt with them very faithfully, all that autumn and winter, though at one time he was so ill with fever from an old wound that he could not sit his horse. The following summer also, he was able to give to the north-east, for English nobles and Edward II were too busy quarrelling about the King's Gascon favourite, Piers Gaveston, to have much attention to spare for Scotland that year, and by June, the only north-eastern castle still in Comyn-Baliol hands was Banff, while in the south, Dundee was still holding out.

That autumn he was busy with Larn and the Lords of the Isles, and at the end of 1308 he had two-thirds of Scotland actively for him, with the Tay for a frontier and all the north for retreat. He had spent a full year dealing with the effects of that dagger-thrust in the Franciscan's Kirk, but now he was free to turn again to the south, where the whole land beyond the Forth was still in English hands.

With James Douglas he set to the task of thrusting the frontier

back, and that March, almost exactly three years after his coronation, he was able to hold his Parliament in St Andrews.

By May, Edward II was gathering his War Host again, but
his mobilisation was slow, his troubles with his nobles and his
favourite many, and it was another full year before he crossed the
Tweed again. And when he did, it was only to be drawn on and
on by The Bruce through country that, having been so often
fought on already, could not feed his troops, until the time came
when he was forced, for very famine, to head south again, with
his rearguard harried by the seemingly invisible Scots troops
behind them.

Indeed most of the next four years went by in long stretches
of stalemate, interspersed with short, sharp outbursts of thrust
and counter-thrust, castles taken and retaken, campaigns as
intricately manœuvred as a game of chess, that somehow never
came to battle. But The Bruce was a master of manœuvre, and
these campaigns too, had their uses, in wearing down the English
armies and lowering their morale, while raising high the hearts of
the Scots behind him. These were years of Scots raids into
England which had to be bought off; years, too, in which the
English King (his father would have wept for shame) tried more
than once for an armistice, though never on the only terms, the
recognition of Scotland's freedom as a separate country, that
The Bruce would consider.

And now, seven years after The Bruce's coronation, came the
Great Year; the year which saw, not final victory, but the crisis
of the long struggle, and the beginning of that final victory still
so many years ahead.

It had begun in the previous summer, with his one remaining
brother, Edward. Edward was besieging Stirling; he had been at
it for three or four months, and it was not the kind of warfare that
appealed to his hot head. So to free himself for something more
exciting, he made a bargain with Mowbray, the Governor, that
he would suspend hostilities if the other swore to surrender
the castle if, within eight days of the next Midsummer's
Day, no English relief force had appeared within three leagues
of it.

That was a gauntlet flung in England's face, and she had lost
too much prestige already to be able to refuse such a challenge;
and after the long years of a war that had half gone to sleep, she
gathered herself together for another mighty effort, while the
Scots set themselves while there was still time, to make sure of
Lothian, the one district of the northern Lowlands that was still

in English hands. Linlithgow Castle fell in September (that's a bonnie story, but there's no room for it here), Roxburgh only a few days later—but the Queen and Marjorie and Lady Buchan had long since been moved elsewhere—and Edinburgh itself went down to a young kinsman of The Bruce's in the spring. By Easter there were only five Scottish castles still in English hands. But England as well as Scotland had grown united, and was determined to teach the other a lesson she should never forget. And that is a dangerous mood for the English to be in.

Edward's preparations were set going very early in the year, since Stirling must at all costs be relieved by midsummer. The Army numbered more than 21,000 English and Welsh, 4,000 Irish archers, and an uncertain number of men-at-arms from the French Provinces; and added to this were 2,500 heavily armed knights. Against such a War Host, The Bruce could raise only 7,000 Foot, no foreign auxiliaries, and not more than 500 light cavalry, for the Scots nobles were accustomed to fight on foot among their men, in a way that seemed most strange to the English knight on his great barded destrier. But his men, unlike many Scots armies before and after them, were superbly disciplined. Nothing shows The Bruce's personality and powers of handling men more clearly than the discipline in a Scots army of seven hundred years ago.

The English moved with the coming of full summer. They crossed the Tweed in mid-June, and marched unopposed down Lauderdale.

Bruce and his Scots had already marched out at the end of May from their training ground in the Tor Wood, and encamped on the high wooded ground south of Stirling, covering the old Roman Road towards the town above where it forded the Bannock Burn. And his scouts came in to him there with news of the English Army's every move.

The sun rose on the morning of Midsummer's Eve, and the heather shimmered in the heat; and to the Scottish soldiers waiting across the road to Stirling, the morning must have seemed long. . . .

Edward had bivouacked at Falkirk for the night, now they were within ten miles of Stirling. And a few miles short of the Bannock crossing they were met by Mowbray, who had slipped round the Scottish flank from Stirling Castle, to warn the King of how the road was held.

It was decided that the main army should halt, and that a body of picked cavalry should get around the Scots by a bridle track

106

below the hill slope, and so lay their claim to the castle without engaging the enemy at all.

The mistake was in not realising that the track brought them for one short stretch into full view of the Scottish Army. Young Randolf, The Bruce's nephew who had taken Edinburgh Castle, charged down with two hundred men to cross their track. The fight, though small, was desperate, and James Douglas, getting leave from The Bruce, took down a reinforcement of his own men; but as they raced down towards the fight, Douglas saw that the English cavalry were beginning to waver, and checked his men, that Randolf should have the full glory of his victory. But the sight of the Scottish reinforcements struck confusion into the already wavering English. They broke and fled, those that were left of them, back to the main body, where their coming spread their own confusion in all directions.

Since it seemed that there was to be no getting round, Edward's Advance Guard of heavy knights pushed on, led by the Earl of Gloucester and the Earl of Hereford. They forded the Bannock Burn, the upward roll of the land ahead masking them and the Scots from each other, though The Bruce, sitting his horse on higher ground, must just have seen them. To their right front was a gentle slope of open ground. They crested it, and found on their right a long advance of open country level as a dancing floor, leading straight towards the upthrust shape of Stirling Castle some two miles away, and on the left front, where the road began to climb, the wooded ridge, with the Scots moving among the trees.

Hereford's nephew, Sir Henry de Bohun, was leading, and not liking the look of the Scots in that position, he signalled his force to fall back on the ford. But in the self-same instant he saw a man ride out from the Scots position, a man in light armour, riding only a little grey hunter, and with the blink of sunlit gold encircling his helmet. That blink of gold could mean only one thing. De Bohun, on his great barded horse, saw his chance to end the war at one stroke, and fewtoring his lance, drove in his spurs and charged.

The Bruce, who had merely changed his position and ridden out for a sight of what the English were doing on that side, was unarmed save for a light axe, and had not even changed the mare he rode on the march for the great war horse he only rode in battle. He sat still and let de Bohun charge, and then at the last instant, in a movement timed like that of a dancer, swung the hunter aside, and rising in his stirrups as de Bohun thundered past after his missed blow, brought the axe crashing down on his helmet. The shaft broke, but the blade had done its work and de Bohun, pitching from the high-peaked saddle, was dead before he hit the ground.

Then followed a sharp set-to, as the Scots broke forward to meet Edward's vanguard, a skirmish in which de Bohun's squire was killed standing valiantly on his lord's body; but the English fell back across the ford, and since his own men were not mounted, The Bruce whistled them back from the chase, and for the moment the thing was ended.

Getting back his breath, the Scottish King turned to Douglas and his other officers, saying, 'I have broken my good axe'. It is a lovely remark; one can hear the wry, regretful amusement, almost the twinkle in it, across seven centuries.

King Edward sat his horse on a little hill behind the English Host, with his leaders about him, and gave his orders. If, as they reported, there was level ground up there between the wooded slopes and the Forth Marshes, they should have space to use the cavalry to the best advantage, and his confidence had risen perilously near to foolhardiness in consequence.

They should get the Army across Bannock Burn tonight, bivouac on the low ground where the plateau sank into the Marshes, and so be ready to attack the ridge at first light to-morrow morning.

The Earl of Gloucester who, though young, was the finest of all the King's commanders, said bluntly that such a course of action was madness. With Bannock and Forth meeting behind them, the whole army would be in a trap with all hope of retreat cut off.

The King said the plan was for advance, not retreat, to which Gloucester returned that plans could occasionally miscarry, and that the men were desperately weary and needed a day's rest before going into action.

The King promptly accused him of cowardice, and young Gloucester said no more.

So the English Host spent the few hours of darkness, when they might have been getting some desperately needed rest, in struggling across the burn into the death-trap waiting for them on the other side.

There was no possibility of crossing where the burn ran through the deep cut of the Bannock Gorge, and when they reached the lower ground and crowded down towards the water, they found themselves floundering in mosses and peat bogs, the horses sinking

108

to the fetlocks, the few waggons that they tried to get through becoming bogged axle-deep. They pulled down the cottages of Bannockburn Village, and with the wattle and thatch, contrived to bridge the morass after a fashion, for horses and men to struggle over. The whole baggage train they left behind on the far side, but even so, the sky was lightening in the east before the last man was across, and even for those who had crossed earlier, there was no rest with the enemy so near. They passed the night in harness, not daring even to unbit and unsaddle the wretched horses.

The major action which the Scots had expected that day had not come off, but in the smaller fight on the plateau, they had borne away the victory. They were outnumbered even more greatly than The Bruce had expected, but now he had to decide at once, whether to make the smaller victory serve for now, and draw off his men and return to the old guerrilla tactics. That would mean almost certain success, but he had seen before that the victories so gained could be inconclusive; or whether to stake everything on one mighty throw, and taking advantage of his strong position and the lowering of the enemy's morale, fight the thing to a finish next day.

He made his choice, with or without the help of a Council of War, and the Scottish Army made ready for battle, and 'Slept on their Spears' in the woods through the short summer night. At dawn, the dawn of Midsummer's Day, which is also the Feast of the Festival of St John the Baptist, the priests, some of them armed beneath their vestments, said Mass. The lesson for the day is the great fortieth chapter of Isaiah: 'Comfort ye, comfort ye, my people. . . . Speak ye comfortably to Jerusalem, and cry unto her that her warfare is accomplished.' Mass over, the Bishop of Inchaffray blessed the Army, and a hurried meal of bannock was issued and eaten.

And now it was time for the onset. The Scots had been divided overnight into four divisions, and while Bruce held his own in reserve under cover of the woods, the other three, under his brother Edward, James Douglas and young Randolf, marched out from the woodshore with banners flying, and headed down the slope towards the plateau. They came in three great Schiltroons, Douglas's between and a little behind the other two. The English trumpets sounded the alarm, and King Edward, sitting his horse on higher ground, saw them come, while his own troops were hurriedly deploying for action in an attempt to get up out of the low ground before the Scots were on them, and said to

Umfraville, a Baliol Scot who was one of his staff officers, 'What! Will these Scots fight!' and then triumphantly, as one of the Schiltroons halted and dropped to their knees, 'See! They kneel to ask for mercy!'

'True enough, but not of you, Sire', said Umfraville curtly.

The English were swarming up the slope, but hampered by having to make haste over such rough ground, and by the pressure of those behind, who could not clearly see what was happening, they were losing formation and becoming confused. The archers, strung along the north side of the gorge, began to pour in their flights of arrows against the Scottish Schiltroons, which were done with praying and on the move again. They were the greatest danger to the Schiltroons, and Bruce, watching from the wood-shore above, must have thought piercingly of Falkirk. But this time he had the answer, and sent out his cavalry from the right, hidden from view until the last moment by a lift in the ground, they drove down on the flank of the English archers, who, with no warning until the charge was almost upon them, broke and fled, spreading still more confusion among the deploying troops.

The Schiltroons were thrusting forward upon the English van, who were being thrust upon almost as hard by their own advancing rear pushing up from behind to join the fighting that they could hear ahead. Young Gloucester, whom yesterday the King had accused of cowardice, led a charge of cavalry which ran disastrously into the fire of the remaining archers, and was killed in the first shock of joining battle. Hereford charged after him, against Edward Bruce on the Scot's Right. The English Right followed suit, and Randolf met them, let them smash on his front like a sea-wave on a rock, and drove on into their midst. And into the gap between the two, thrust James Douglas, closing the moving wall of the Scots attack.

The English were pinned helplessly by the Bannock gorge on their left, and their own reserves in the rear, the whole mass became hopelessly jammed, three-quarters of them unable to reach the enemy at all. Two hundred English knights never drew their swords for lack of chance to use them.

Then out of the woods, The Bruce led his reserves, to strike in on the English flank, and under the impact, the mass of men and horses broke. The steady pressure of the Scots drove them back and left-hand wise, crushing them down against the edge of the Bannock gorge, and the struggling mass must have hung there like water that rises and clings to itself before it spills over the lip of a tilted cup. Then they went over, mailed, desperate men and terror-maddened stallions, in a scrambling, slithering, shrieking flood.

Panic was running through the rest in good earnest now, and the shout went up from the Scots, 'On them! They fail!' and then a great raw yelling from another quarter, and down from the woods swept the Irregulars, the untrained troops and camp followers held in reserve until that moment, howling like demons, with banners made from the camp blankets and pikes and tent poles and butcher's cleavers in their hands.

It was the last horror.

Edward's staff saw the position lost beyond all hope, saw also that there could be no going back the way they had come, and bent all their efforts to getting the King clear, by way of the track below the hill that led to Stirling. The sight of the Royal Standard in flight completed the havoc. The English broke hideously, into a fleeing mob with nowhere to flee to. Many were trapped in the death-gorge, some got across over the very bodies of their comrades, some streamed after the King towards Stirling; many and many broke through their own rear, and carried it away with them to be drowned in the burn or trampled into the quaking peat-moss.

Edward's bodyguard, some hundreds strong, cut their way out, forcing the King in their midst—he was a fool, but no coward, and would have stayed to share the fate of his Army—and when they were clear, Sir Giles de Agentine, who had ridden at the King's side, released his bridle, and said, 'I am not used to flee, and I will not now', turned back and spurred towards the Scots, to fall in the thick of the struggle. He stands as the hero of the English side that day.

The King got safely away, not to Stirling, which must now, by the terms of the agreement, be yielded up to Bruce, but to Dunbar, harried all the way by Sir James Douglas and a handful of cavalry. And from Dunbar he took ship to Bamburgh.

Even after the battle, the toll of English casualties was not all done. Bruce's cavalry were too few for effective pursuit of such a flying Host, but the Border was a long way off, and though The Bruce's own treatment of prisoners was unexpectedly gentle, the countryside had old scores to settle, and even the women closed in for the kill.

Many prisoners were taken, Umfraville and Hereford among them. In some cases their ransoms came in handy to refill the Scottish war-chest while in others they were exchanged for captive Scots. For Hereford, the Bruce received back his Queen and little

Marjorie, his sister Christina, and old Bishop Wishart, now blind. There is no word of Lady Buchan, and it seems she must have died in captivity.

The war was not yet ended. Indeed it dragged on for another fourteen years. But from that Midsummer Day, Scotland was cleared of the English, and was never overrun again, until the day, thirty-five years after Edward I laid claim to be its Liege Lord, when peace was signed at last, and sealed at Berwick by the marriage of The Bruce's little son, Prince David, with the six-year-old Princess of England, Joan Make-Peace.

But neither King was present at that wedding, the King of England for reasons that don't need much explaining, The Bruce, because he was mortally ill.

Some say it was leprosy, but in mediaeval times almost any severe skin disease went by that name. And there is no record that he was ever set apart, as a leper, even one who was also a king, would have been set apart from his fellow men. Also it was something that killed more quickly than leprosy has ever done.

Whatever it was, he knew that he was dying, and in early June, 1329, he set his affairs in order and saw his lords do homage to the son who was to succeed him. Then he called closer Sir James Douglas, for they were still together, as they had been through so many years, and (so Froissart tells)

Said before all the Lords, Sir James my dear friend, ye know well that I have had much ado in my day to uphold and sustain the right of this realm, and when I had most ado, I made a solemn vow, the which as yet I have not accomplished, whereat I am right sorry. The which was, if I might achieve and make an end to all my wars, so that I might once have brought this realm in rest and peace, that I promised in my mind to have gone and warred on Christ's enemies, adversaries to our holy Christian Faith. To this purpose my mind hath ever intended, but Our Lord would not consent to this, for I have had so much ado in my days, and now in my last enterprise, I have taken such a malady that I cannot escape. And sith it is so that my body cannot go nor achieve that my heart desireth, I will send the heart instead of the body to accomplish mine avow; and because I know not in all my realm no knight more valiant than ye be, nor of body so well furnished to accomplish mine avow, therefore I require you, mine own dear and special friend, that ye will take on you this voyage for the love of me, and to acquit my soul against my Lord God. For I trust so much in your nobleness and truth, that an ye will take on you, I doubt not but ye shall achieve it, and then shall I die in more ease and quiet. I will that as soon as I am trespassed out of this world that ye take the heart out of my body and embalm it, and take of my treasure as ye shall think sufficient for that enterprise both for yourself and for such company as ye will take with you, and present my heart to the Holy Sepulchre where Our Lord lay, seeing my body cannot come there. . . .

Then all the Lords that heard these words wept for pity, and when this knight Sir James Douglas might speak for weeping, he said, 'Ah gentle and noble King, a hundred times I thank Your Grace of the great honour that ye do to me, sith of so noble and great treasure ye put me in charge. And Sir, I shall do with a glad heart, all that ye have commanded me, to the best of my true power. . . .' 'Then I thank you', said the King, 'for now I shall die in more ease of my mind, sith that I know that the most worthy and sufficient knight of my realm shall achieve for me that which I never could attain unto.' And then soon after this the noble Robert de Brus trespassed out of this uncertain world, his heart was taken out of his body and embalmed, and honourably he was interred in the Abbey of Dunfermline, in the year of Our Lord God MCCCXXIX, the VII day of the month of November.

Sir James Douglas, true to his trust, set off in the spring with The Bruce's heart in a silver casket; but neither he nor it ever reached the Holy Sepulchre, for on the way, turning aside to give his aid to the King of Spain against the Saracens in Granada, he was killed charging at the head of his little company, shouting the old Clan war cry 'Douglas! Douglas!' with his last breath.

The only one of the little band of Scots knights to survive—and he had been kept out of the fighting with a broken arm—had his body embalmed, and brought it and the King's heart home to Scotland. Douglas was laid among his own folk in Douglasdale, The Bruce's heart in the Abbey of Melrose, which he loved in life; for both of them, their crusading done.

Chapter 9

Owen Glyndwr

IT is a hundred years and more since the last flare of Welsh freedom went out, and Prince Llewellin's head, crowned with ivy leaves, was set up on its pike-shaft above the ramparts of the Tower.

Wales has grown quiet under the English yoke, indeed it has almost ceased to feel like a yoke, through the long years of companionship in arms, during which Welsh soldiers have fought in their thousands beside English in the French wars. Why, a full third of the victorious army at Crècy were Welshmen! But the hands of the Marcher Lords are still heavy, and under the new comradeship, Welshmen still remember that they are Welsh, not English, and that once they were free under their own Princes. Old fires still smoulder among the hills, waiting to flare again.

It is a hundred years since William Wallace died in Smithfield Market, not yet seventy that The Bruce's heart has lain in Melrose Abbey, and another country gentleman farms his land and rides hawking and listens to the harpers telling old tales beside the evening fire. Tales, maybe, of that very Llewellin, the last Lord of free Wales, whose blood, according to the proud family tradition, runs in his own veins.

His name is Owen Glyndwr.

There were great and strange portents when he was born, the kind of portents that belong to the birth of Heroes. On his birth night the horses in his father's stable were found standing up to their fetlocks in blood, and Shakespeare was following old traditions when he makes him say

> *At my birth*
> *The front of Heaven was full of fiery shapes;*
> *The goats ran from the mountains, and the herds*
> *Were strangely clamorous to the frighted fields.*
> *These signs have marked me extraordinary,*
> *And all the courses of my life do show*
> *I am not in the roll of common man.*

But now he was forty, and though he had not lacked for adventure—he had been shield-squire to Henry Bolingbroke, and after Henry's banishment, to Richard II himself, and went with Richard on that ill-fated Irish expedition which in the long run cost him his crown—he had found time in between whiles to marry and beget children, and keep the fields of his Powys Manor in good heart. And now that Richard was deposed, captured or dead, no one seemed sure which, his future looked to lie quiet enough among his quiet meadows, Sycherth looking towards the Berwin mountains, his mill, his orchard and vineyard, with the pigeons crooling in the well-stocked dovecote, and the old house alive with young sons and still unmarried daughters.

But Sycherth was not his only estate; he possessed also Glyndyfrdwy among the wild wooded hills where the Vale of Edeymion and Llangollen meet. And a certain upland stretch of the Glyndyfrdwy land over which he and Reginald Grey, Lord of Ruthin, had been falling out for years, was to provide at last the spark that set the old fires blazing again.

The Marcher Lords were a greedy and ungentle class, and Lord Grey of Ruthin was probably the worst of them, as he was certainly one of the most powerful. Back in Richard II's time, he had helped himself to the disputed stretch of land, quite simply on the grounds that its borders marched with his own. Glyndwr carried the dispute to the King's Court in London and won his case, and Lord Grey, raging at the humiliation of this defeat at the hands of a wild Welshman, had hated the other since that day, with a hate out of all proportion to the size of the original dispute.

Then, with Richard gone, and Bolingbroke no longer Bolingbroke but Henry IV, Lord Grey seized the stretch of land again, and again Owen Glyndwr took his case before the King. But Henry had small love left for the man who, because he had a wife and children to care for had chosen not to go into exile with him, and he dismissed the case out of hand, though one of his chief Councillors, Bishop Trevor, himself a Welshman, warned him of such a flagrant injustice to a man who, for all his small state, had Llewellin blood in him and a surprising amount of power and popularity among his own kind.

The Welsh were already in a dangerous mood. They had always resented English rule, but oddly, they had loved Richard with the unreasonable strength of personal loyalty that the Celt knows well. They were not even sure that Richard was dead; the body shown to the London crowds might have been the body of

116

someone like him, and if he were not dead, then he was still their King and Henry no more than a usurper. If he *were* dead, then in one way or the other, Henry was his murderer. In either case, they never for one instant considered Henry as the rightful King of England, and when they rose in revolt, as they were to do presently, Richard's cause was mingled in their minds and hearts with the cause of free Wales.

The hands of the Marcher Lords grew heavier yet, the Welsh more restless under it. And into this already angry and bewildered Wales Glyndwr returned from London in the kind of rage that can be imagined, and the countryside raged with him. But there was worse to come at Lord Grey's hands. The King was at that time preparing for yet another expedition against the Scots, and among the rest of the nobles and gentlemen, he summoned Owen Glyndwr to his standard. The summons was sent through Lord Grey as Chief Marcher of North Wales; and Lord Grey did not pass it on until it was too late for Glyndwr either to join the King's Army or send reason why he could not come. The King promptly assumed that Glyndwr was a rebel, and added his name to those of some wild spirits who had lately been cattle raiding and making small-scale trouble along the border. Grey got leave to move against him and confiscate his estate, along with those of the other trouble-makers. It may have been the old hate working in him, it may have been because with Wales in its present state of unrest, he felt that it would be wise to get rid of a man so powerful among his fellows, and who must, he knew well, be burning with a sense of injustice.

Whichever his reason, the result was the same. Grey gathered his forces and joined by a fellow Marcher, Earl Talbot of Clink, marched on Owen at Sycherth so unexpectedly that he only just had time to escape to the woods before the house was surrounded. And from shelter of the trees, he watched his beloved home go up in flames. That summer's day's work filled not only Owen's cup but all Wales' to the brim. But angry as Wales was, she might have done no more than grumble and raid the English borders if she had not had a leader at this touch-and-go time. But thanks to Lord Grey and the King, the leader that was all she needed, was there to hand.

Owen Glyndwr raised his standard at Glyndwr; the standard bearing the ancient Red Dragon of Wales that had been the Red Dragon of Britain in Arthur's day. And to him there and at the ancient British camp of Caer Drewin, near by, all the wilder spirits who had been raiding along the border, and a host of others who, sickened of Norman oppression, were suddenly and for the first time eager to take up arms. Each man brought his own weapons, and being used to tribal warfare among themselves, they were no pitchfork army. From the vales of Edeymon and Llangollen, from the wild uplands of Bryn Eglwys, from the far shores of Lake Bala, they came in like mountain spate, the bards at their heads carrying not only their harps but the mighty long-bows of war. Ancient prophecies were remembered. Had not Merlin himself said that once again a Welsh Prince should wear the Crown of all Britain? There were strange portents in sea and sky; men remembered and told again how the horses had been found standing fetlock-deep in blood on the night this tall man in squire's war-gear had been born. At the end of August, Owen declared himself Prince of Wales, and made his first move. It was, not surprisingly, against Lord Grey.

Choosing a Fair-day, he fell upon the little town of Ruthin at the foot of the great Marcher's castle and made a clean sweep of all the stock collected in the Market Square, then raced on east-ward through Shropshire harrying and burning the homes of the English settlers, leaving a trail of strongpoints sacked to tell of their passing.

Word of the revolt reached Henry on the Scottish Border, and he raced south, summoning the Sheriffs of the midland counties to join him with their levies, and was in Shrewsbury by the end of September.

Meanwhile, Owen, hearing of the King's approach, had turned back on his own trail of ruin. And after waiting some days at Shrewsbury with no whiff of the Welsh War Host, Henry deter-mined to follow them into Wales, sure of crushing Glyndwr and his irregulars without much trouble. He marched through Wales to Anglesey, drove out the Minorite Friars from the Abbey of Llanfaes as being supporters of Owen's, and within a month, driven by bad weather and lack of supplies, was back in Worcester, never having caught the least sight of the Welsh war bands, who had simply melted into the mountains of the Snowdon range, and left him to hunt for them to his heart's content.

Henry issued a general pardon to all Welshmen who came to report for it, saving only Glyndwr himself, but scarcely anybody bothered to come for it, and the King, still not thinking much of the Welsh rising, spent the winter in London entertaining the Greek Emperor. In the early spring, Parliament published certain ordinances for the future government of the Principality. In future, no Welshman was to be a Justice, Chamberlain, Chancellor,

Chief Forester, Sheriff or Constable of a castle. They were to be taxed and charged with repairing and maintaining all walls, gates and castles when wilfully destroyed. No meetings of the Welsh were to be held without permission of the Chief Officers of the Lordship. There was to be no marrying between Welsh and English, and the men of the Marches might take any revenge they liked on a Welshman who owed them money. Sharpest wound of all to the Welsh pride, they were no longer to maintain their bards, which meant not only the loss of old songs and Hero-tales, but the memory of their past, since the bards were the carriers of the nation's history. Wales' very soul was being threatened by the English, and the ancient hatred of the Celt for the Saxon woke again.

That winter the forbidden bards, harp on shoulder and bow or sword in hand, came pouring in to Owen, where he held Royal Court at Glyndwr. The thing spread far beyond the Marches, and in Oxford Welsh students sold their books to buy a sword and set out for the border.

Young Prince Hal had been left by his father to keep his head-quarters at Chester, with Harry Hotspur, son of old Northumberland as constable of half a dozen castles and Justice of North Wales, and a clash between them and Glyndwr was inevitable before long. That spring the rebel leader, having roused enough feeling in the north had turned southward and was raging through Central Wales. Hotspur went after him, and they came to battle at the foot of Cader Idris, a battle that ended with no clear-cut victory for either side. Indeed it must have been a rather half-hearted fight from the first, for on one side there was an ancient friendship between Glyndwr and the Percy's, and on the other, Hotspur was so disgusted with the King for having failed to send him either much-needed reinforcements or the money to pay his troops, that he resigned all his Welsh appointments immediately afterwards and flung off back to Northumberland.

Owen had now raised his dragon standard on the rounded crest of Plynlimmon, and the south, that had until now lain quiet, flocked to him there as the north had done. With these first-comers, he crossed the head-water of the Wye and Severn, and came driving down upon the Marches of Carmarthen, and as he went, the common folk, though not yet the gentles, rose on every hand to join his War Host and follow him as he swept on as though on dragon wings of fire through the English-held lands of South and Mid-Wales. Once, he and five hundred of his men were surrounded by more than three times their number from the old Flemish Colonies, but under his leadership they cut their way out, leaving two hundred Flemish dead behind them; and that personal feat of arms brought him five thousand new recruits. So like a swollen torrent he roared down the Severn Valley, burning Montgomerie on the way, sweeping all before him, until, where the Severn bursts out into the rich lowlands of Shropshire, the great red castle of Powys barred his way, and dammed the flood at last and flung it back.

But setbacks and sallies against him from the castles which studded South Wales could do little to hold him from the open country between them. By late August, Owen was free of the open country from the Marches to the seas; he had spread terror along the border, and messengers rode hard to the King with panic-stricken pleas for help, from beleaguered Marchers and frightened Abbots. (There was no love lost between Owen and the Church.)

The King came, and in early October he and Prince Hal marched with a large army into Wales. As before, there was no sign of an armed Welshman in the length and breadth of the land. The barns were bare, the small black cattle and mountain sheep had disappeared into the hills. Henry marched around Wales for a while, gutted another monastery on the plea that three of the brothers had sympathised with Glyndwr, stabled his horses at the High Altar. . . . Owen's troops at last began to show themselves, or at least to make themselves felt, harrying the flanks and outposts of the Royal Army, but when Henry tried to bring them to action, he might as well have tried to grapple with the hill mist. By the end of the month he was back at Shrewsbury, leaving Wales rather encouraged than otherwise, behind him.

Owen headed north again and went into winter quarters at his own Manor of Glyndwr. He erupted out again in January for a fight with his old enemy Lord Grey of Ruthin, cut his forces to pieces, took him captive and held him to ransom for ten thousand marks, which took a year to get together and left him a poor man for life.

That winter also, Owen was sending letters asking for aid to the Kings of Scotland, Ireland and even France.

That spring, 1402, started with a bang, a fiery comet in the sky, great thunderstorms and all kinds of strange happenings throughout the country. In one place, while the people were in church, lightning struck the roof and the Devil entered dressed as a Franciscan Friar (the one Order that was friendly to Owen) and leapt three times over the Altar, then turning black in the face, rushed

120

down the aisle actually diving between the legs of a man who got in his way, and leaving an overpowering smell of sulphur behind him.

But despite the portents, there was something of a lull, until late in May, Owen descended on the borders of Hereford and savaged the lands of the young Earl of March, who, descending from Edward III was the rightful heir to the English throne. Henry, not unnaturally kept the boy close in his charge, leaving his estates to be handled by his young uncle, Edmund Mortimer. And Mortimer who was a fine soldier, gathered his fellow Marcher Lords and advanced to meet the Welsh. They came together in a narrow valley, the Welsh led that time by Rhys Ap Gethin, one of Owen's most dangerous captains. The English Army was overthrown, and Mortimer himself was captured—a captive of much more actual importance than Grey of Ruthin, but bringing less personal satisfaction to Glyndwr because there was no bad blood between them.

Meantime, while Glyndwr was besieging the castles on the Carnarvon and Merioneth coasts, the King had enough work both in Ireland and on the Scottish borders to keep his hands full. But by July 23rd he was in Shropshire, and provisions, arms, and men for a fresh assault, were pouring through Welshpool, Ludlow and Montgomerie, Hereford, Shrewsbury and Chester. By the end of August, three great armies stood ready under the command of the King himself, Prince Hal and the Earl of Warwick. And a week later, they crossed the border. To the rest of England it must really have looked as though the troubles with Wales were at an end.

Until now, they had half, but only half, believed that Owen Glyndwr was a wizard; within a week they were convinced that he was the Devil himself. Never had there been such a September in the Welsh mountains. Storm and tempest broke around them, the very skies descended in sheeting rain upon the heads of the English armies. The rivers became roaring torrents and swept the fords away. Tents were blown flat, provisions ruined, and night after night the soldiers slept in the open half starved and drenched to the skin so that numbers died from exposure, while the thunder roared as though the very mountains were angry and the lightning leapt against them out of inky skies. Within a fortnight they had to pull back, and there was not a living English soldier, save for the castle garrisons, left in Wales.

Two months later young Mortimer, still a captive in name, married Owen's youngest daughter, Jane, and a fortnight later still, he wrote to his own tenants, telling them that he had joined Glyndwr's cause, and calling on them for their help and support.

No need to follow in detail the burnings and harryings of that summer. They made Glyndwr's name a terror throughout the Marches. Beacons stood ready to light on every hill-top to give warning of the Welshman's coming, and men were trembling far into the midland counties. Even in the eastern part of England they knew for sure that he would soon be into Northampton; the monks of St Albans hung on the chancel wall a supplication to Almighty God to save them from Glyndwr and the Welsh. Appeal after appeal went to the King, each more urgent and panic stricken than the last, and all the time the King was busy with his Scots wars, and Prince Hal was stuck in Shrewsbury, unable to move for lack of anything in his war-chest.

In July, with breathtaking suddenness (but many secret messengers must have passed in the weeks before) the Percies came out into revolt against the King, and the old Earl being sick at the time, Harry Hotspur swept his troops south to join Owen and young Mortimer. The King acted then with incredible swiftness. Hs sent out urgent orders to the Sheriffs of the midland counties, for a call-out of their levies, and within five days he and the Prince entered Shrewsbury with close on thirty thousand men at their backs. When Hotspur, warned of his coming, reached the city gates that evening with fifteen thousand, he found the Royal Standard flying from the castle tower. He had expected Glyndwr to meet him there, but there was no sign of his coming, and desperately outnumbered as he was, Hotspur had no choice but to give battle without the expected reinforcement. Next day at Heyteley Field, three miles north of Shrewsbury, was fought the bloodiest battle that England had seen since Norman William marched to Hastings. And when the red sunset came, Prince Hal, who had played a hero's part all day, had lost four thousand men and lay sore hurt with his face laid open by an arrow, and Harry Hotspur lay cold among the English dead like a boar among the hounds that he has slain before they pulled him down.

And all the while, far off in Carmarthen, Owen Glyndwr knew nothing of what had happened, for Hotspur's urgent summons had never reached him.

If the King had struck on into Wales then, it might have been the end of the three-year-old revolt, for the Welsh were shaken to their roots by the defeat, but he had to turn north again to deal with old Northumberland's rising, and by the time he got back to Wales in September, Owen had steadied his followers once more,

122

and made a clean sweep of Hereford, and the Battle of Shrewsbury, save for the terrible loss of lives, might never have been.

The King made another of his thrusts into Wales, but it was too late, and lasted fewer days than the earlier ones, and almost before he was back in England, all traces of this latest attempt had disappeared like footprints in the sand when the tide is coming in. Indeed, considering how great a soldier he was, and the strength of his hand elsewhere, it really does seem as though some spell lay over him whenever he turned to Wales.

In the following spring, Glyndwr took Harlech, the most remote of all the English held castles, and bringing his family to join him, made his headquarters there on the rocky headland above the Western Sea, where a long line of Welsh chieftains out of the farmost mists of the past had held court centuries before the Norman Castle rose there or even the Legions marched from Rome.

Summer followed the same pattern of fire and sword, and before the end of it the Shropshire Marches were so hard pressed that the Council of the Kingdom had to yield to their desperate appeal for leave to make terms with Owen on their account and pay him what he demanded in exemption money. Powys and Aberystwith had fallen soon after Harlech. Castle after castle went the same way, and the winter which followed, the grey rock and the grey tower of Harlech must have known scenes worthy of any that had gone before in the great days of the chieftains; with Glyndwr at the very high tide of his power, holding his court there with his councillors, his warriors and his bards about him.

One wonders what Owen's thought can have been that winter. He had a summer that had been one long string of victories behind him, but save for Anglesey, Carnarvonshire and Western Pembroke, Wales and the Marches lay in ruins from end to end, and his hands were red with Welsh blood as well as English. It had been deliberately done, like the carrying out of The Bruce's scorched earth policy, and with the same intention of making a land too bare to support an invader, but it cannot have been a pleasant thing for the man who had done it to think of in the dark hours of the winter nights.

And this winter was indeed Owen Glyndwr's high tide. With the spring, very slowly, the tide began to turn.

It started with a battle between Rhys Ap Gethin and Prince Hal at Grosmont, in which the Welsh suffered a most bloody defeat and left eight hundred dead behind them when they fled the field. It went on when Glyndwr, rushing up fresh forces, to try to retrieve the position, met the Prince advancing triumphantly into Wales, and was thrashed again, this time with the loss of fifteen hundred men, and Owen's young son Griffith on his first war trail, who was captured and carried back to the Tower.

Once again it might have been the end, but once again the King on the point of following up his son's success, was called north to handle a fresh uprising of old Northumberland and the Percy clan. And while he was away, five thousand French troops (Owen had been treaty-making in the past winter) landed in South Wales and joined forces with the Welshman.

With the French, commanded by the Sire de Hugueville at his shoulder then, Glyndwr turned at once on the Anglo-Flemish town of Haverfordwest, and took and burned it; then pushed on, leaving the usual trail of ruin behind him, to arrive at the gates of Worcester in the self-same hour as the King returning from the north.

There might have been another Shrewsbury, fierce and decisive, but instead the two armies encamped some way outside the town, the French and Welsh in the old British fort on the crest of Woodbury Hill, the King's Army on the ridge northward, and there, both in such perfect defensive positions that each feared to move out to the attack, they confronted each other for eight days across the valley between. And down into the valley, from time to time, spurred bands of hotheads from either side, to skirmish or even fight out single combats of their own in full view of both armies. It must have been almost like a tournament, and just about as pointlessly wasteful in terms of human life. About five hundred men in all died during those eight days.

The whole performance sounds as crazy as the Mad Hatter's tea party; but in fact, the King showed his wisdom in not going into open battle. He had (for once) ample provisions behind him, and was all the while growing in strength as his fresh levies had time to gather. And Glyndwr and Hugueville, running short of supplies and with a wasted country behind them, and with their Northumberland allies already crushed also had good reasons for refusing open battle. In the end the Welsh struck camp first, and began the long march back. The King tried to give chase, but found as usual that the hills were on Glyndwr's side, and after eighteen of his supply waggons were captured by the hungry Welsh, was forced to call off the hunt.

Back in Hereford, he gathered his forces afresh, and set out on his fifth invasion of Wales. It was the same story all over again, even to the weather.

But in the winter, the Welsh and French fell out, and two-thirds of the French went home; a little later both Anglesey and the Vale of Towy fell away from Glyndwr from sheer war-weariness and lack of the where-with-all to go on living, and their loss must have struck coldly on Owen's heart.

After that comes a misty time in the story, when history knows nothing of Glyndwr, and only little gleams of legend here and there prick the mist. From them it seems that he took to the heather, maybe to gain some first-hand idea of the spirit of his followers at that time. There is a story of how Sir Lawrence Berkrolles, the Lord of Coity Castle, one day received a visitor, a quiet gentleman, unarmed and accompanied by only one servant, who asked him for a night's lodging. The Marcher made him welcome, and took such a liking to him that he pressed him to stay on for a few days—for if he did so, he might actually see the great Owen Glyndwr himself, as it was murmured he was in the neighbourhood, and all the free men of the castle were out hunting him. The pleasant stranger accordingly stayed, but at the end of three days, there being still no sign of the promised capture, he said regretfully that he must be on his way. His host rode with him a short distance to set him on his way, and at parting, the guest held out a hand to him saying, 'Owen Glyndwr as a sincere friend, having neither hatred, treachery nor deception in his heart, gives his hand to Sir Lawrence Berkrolles, and thanks him for his kindness and the generous reception which he and his friend, in the guise of a servant, have experienced from him at his castle.'

And so saying, struck spurs to his horse and was away, with his faithful follower, before the Lord of Coity could so much as cry out.

Early in 1407, he seems to have been back with his troops, yet still the mist hangs about him and there is no clear picture. But through all the scraps of the picture that emerge in letters, orders and traditions, one can sense the deepening shadow, the loss of heart among his own people, the gain of heart among the English. The King, hard pressed from France, and already a sick man, would have taken advantage of this new feeling by flinging in yet another frontal attack in the hope of making a quick finish. Prince Hal protested; he and his captains understood Welsh warfare far better than his father did; the thrust of great armies through the country had failed miserably and would fail as miserably again; it was simply the wrong method for that country and that people. The slower way, the steady pressure of armed

126

bands on the front and flanks of Glyndwr's Army, and the offer of generous terms to all supporters who deserted him and came in for pardon, were the only means of wearing him down.

But the King was the King, and his word the final word. That autumn the Prince, obeying his orders, led an all-out attack on Aberystwith Castle, which, with Harlech, lying midway between Owen's still loyal hunting grounds in the north and south were in some sort the key to the situation. A picked force of more than two thousand archers and men-at-arms was to join the hard core for the border levies; great guns were sent rumbling down from Yorkshire, drawn by straining teams of oxen, and shipped from Bristol to the Cardigan coast, with great store of bow staves and bowstring arrows, stone-shot, sulphur and saltpetre. Through the Forest of Dean along the banks of the Severn, the mighty oaks came crashing down to furnish the beams of siege engines. And the King himself was to be there to watch the final fall of Aberystwith and Harlech and Owen Glyndwr.

But cannon and wooden towers and the flower of the English knighthood were powerless against a castle that Edward I had made impregnable for the holding down of the Welsh, held by a picked garrison of Welshmen under Owen's Lieutenant Rhys Ap Griffith (Owen himself was not there. He could not risk being taken like a fox in a trap, and neither besiegers nor besieged knew where he was). Prince Hal found the castle invulnerable to assault, and sat down to starve it out. The garrison, preparing to starve, knew that their only hope was in Glyndwr coming to relieve them, and surrounded by such a host, the chance of that seemed small enough. Starvation crept upon them, and sickness with it, and in mid-September, Rhys suggested a compromise. The leaders of both sides met, heard Mass, and took Holy Communion together, and afterwards drew up an agreement by which the Welsh were to deliver up the castle by November 1st, if by then Owen had not appeared with a relief force. (A strange echo of Stirling and Bannockburn, a century ago.) Prince Hal, thankful to get away from such a deadly monotonous task, left only five hundred soldiers in camp to see that the agreed armistice was kept—no one expected to see Glyndwr, who had not been heard of for a long while—and returned to England until the time came to receive the castle's surrender.

But in an October mist, with only a week of the time to run, Owen slipped into the castle from the sea with a relief force, and the right to repudiate the whole agreement. There was little the five hundred English could do about it; it was too late in the year for a new campaign, and Owen remained lord of the west coast castles through another winter.

That winter was the most terrible in living memory; a white winter of bitter cold, and the land seemed dead under its drifts from before Christmas to the end of March. But with spring, the snow still lying thick in the north corries of the hills, Glyndwr was again on the war trail, and while he was free, and successful even as a guerrilla leader, England could never hold Wales. But he was no longer a danger to the peace of England nor to Henry's throne. The fragments of the story are told in a different way now; in entries in public records, an order to prevent supplies getting to the rebels, a caution to keep the beacon fires of Cheshire and Shropshire ready for kindling, notes of Lord Marchers trying to come to terms with rebellious tenants; no more panic-stricken messages from beleaguered castle; and though the border counties could not yet sleep easy in their beds, Northampton no longer lay wakeful in fear of the Welsh.

Aberystwith, besieged again, finally fell in the autumn; Harlech held out a few weeks longer; Edmund Mortimer who commanded that garrison, died during the siege, of long privation on top of old wounds; and when it fell at last, his young wife and her mother both fell into the King's hands and were swept off to London. Owen Glyndwr never saw his wife and daughter again.

The shadows were closing over him now, and of the last six years of his life, scarcely any trace remains. His cause was hopelessly lost; he was no longer a mighty Prince, but a leader of guerrilla bands, and the bands grew fewer and smaller. There must have been many in Wales who hated him, then, looking round at their ruined land, feeling the weight of new and harsher English laws on their neck. And Owen? He was growing old; his friends and comrades were dead and maybe their ghosts walked at his heels; his wife and children were lost, his cause was lost; his castles were the mountain caves of Snowdon and Merioneth. But from them he still made fierce and rapid raids upon the northern Marches. He had believed in the justice of his cause and had the courage of his belief, and he had ruined Wales in fighting for it. Yes, he must have been well hated. But as the wounds began to heal over, men forgot the ruin and remembered certain glories that at his coming had woken from their long sleep; they began to see the Hero-light playing like summer lightning round his head. And at least he never laid it down to become mere mortal again as Hereward did.

When Prince Hal became Henry V he issued a pardon to all

Welsh rebels including Owen Glyndwr, but the old eagle clung to his crag, refusing to ask or receive favours from the English, striking still whenever the chance offered, with the few followers left to him. But the blows grew less and less frequent, and at last the mist closes over all.

They will show you his grave in the churchyard at Monrington but no one knows if it is really he who lies there. . . .

'In 1415, Owen disappeared so that neither sight nor tidings of him could be obtained in the country.'

Says one Welsh chronicler:

It was rumoured that he escaped in the guise of a reaper bearing a sickle, according to the tidings of the last who saw and knew him, after which little or no information transpired respecting him nor the place or name of his concealment. The prevalent opinion was that he died in a wood in Glamorgan, but occult chroniclers assert that he and his men still live and are asleep on their arms in a cave called Ogof Dinas in the Vale of Gwent, where they will continue until England is self-abased, when they will sally forth, and, recognising their country's privileges, will fight for the Welsh, who shall be dispossessed of them no more until the Day of Judgment, when the Earth shall be consumed with fire and so reconstructed that neither oppression nor devastation shall take place any more, and blessed will he be who will see that time.

Chapter 10

Montrose

RICHARD III dies on Bosworth Field, and Henry Tudor, Earl of Richmond, claws out his crown from a hawthorn tree, and is proclaimed Henry VII. The ancient and mediaeval worlds are past, and with them the age of Heroes, and overnight the modern world comes in.

Yet now, more than a hundred years later, when the whole Tudor dynasty has come and gone and the Stewarts sit on the throne of England and Scotland, suddenly here is one more of the breed. 'James Graham, 1st Marquis of Montrose, born 1612, died 1650' say the textbooks.

Young Jamie Graham, son of the 4th Earl of Montrose, loved horses and hounds and hawks, and was as wild as a hawk himself, with the kind of wildness that found kindred spirits and drew life-long friends to him, from his schooldays; and life-long enemies, too. His favourite colour was scarlet, his favourite book Sir Walter Raleigh's great *History of the World*. He was educated at St Andrews, where his most notable achievement was to win the silver archery medal, which for five years before his coming had been won by Archibald Campbell, Lord Lorne, who would be the Earl of Argyll and Chief of the greatest of all the Highland clans when his father died. Young Lorne had left St Andrews now, and it should not have mattered to him who won the archery contest after he was gone. But Lord Lorne was a twisted, bitter and unhappy creature, with a perpetual grievance against life which he felt in some way did not treat him as he deserved. He was a nervous horseman, and he could not hold his own with his fellows at any sport that demanded speed or skill of foot, for he was slightly lame. Archery was the only thing that he was really good at; he had rejoiced to the core of his narrow, joyless little soul in those five silver archery medals, and that anyone else should win the medal after him seemed somehow to belittle his own achievement. He would have been very ready to hate whoever it was who had done that, and Jamie Graham with his gift for making friends, and his valiant joy in living was so exactly what Archibald Campbell knew in his heart of hearts he would have given anything to be. . . .

But Jamie Graham knew nothing of that. He gave a celebration party to all his friends, and when there was nothing more to eat or drink and they had danced their brogues off their feet to the music of a street piper, swept them all outside to see which of them could shoot his arrow the highest over St Salvator's Tower. Jamie himself won, but late though it was, the Provost happened to be walking along the street on the far side of the church and the descending arrow went through his hat. There was a certain amount of unpleasantness, and Jamie was sent down for a while.

He was barely seventeen when he married a girl he had known all his life, Magdelen, daughter of Lord Carnegie of Kinnaird Castle. And a portrait of the young Earl (he was Montrose now, his father having died some years before) painted at that time for his bride, shows a young man with a stubborn chin just redeemed from heaviness by the quirk of the eyebrows, and the kind of upward clown's curl at the corners of the sensitive mouth. He is looking grave for the portrait painter, but the face is alight with a reckless humour behind the gravity. Only the eyes are grave all through.

Two years after that portrait was painted, Charles I came north for his long delayed Scottish Coronation, but the young Earl was not in Edinburgh with his fellow nobles, to be presented to him. He was overseas hunting for an adored younger sister who had run away with a married man. At least, that was what took him out of Scotland just at the time the King was coming north, but after he had given up all hope of finding her, he remained abroad, travelling in Europe. He was away three years, while Magdelen waited for him, as she was to spend so much of her life waiting. Jamie, their second son was rising three years old before his father ever saw him.

When he did return—not to Scotland, but to England first, in the year that John Hampton went to gaol for refusing to pay the third levy of ship money—and was presented to the King in Hampton Court Gardens, mischief had been made between them and it was too late. He got a chilly hand to kiss, and nothing more, and rode home in a furious temper, to find Scotland seething with unrest. The King and Archbishop Laud had set themselves to smash the Presbyterian religion and bring the Scottish Church into line with the English. He was trying to foist bishops

131

on to a people who regarded all bishops as the emissaries of the Pope and the Pope as an emissary of the Devil, and who felt beside, that the interference with their way of worship just because it was different from the English way was a deadly threat to their national liberties. Now he had issued, entirely on his own authority, a book of Canons which were to govern the ritual of the Church from now on, and had ordered that a liturgy to be published next year was to be used in all churches.

In Edinburgh the proclamation was read from the steps of the Market Cross in front of the Tolbooth. The liturgy was read for the first time in St Giles Cathedral on July 23rd, 1627, and caused an immediate riot during which one woman flung her stool at the Bishop's head. It resulted in the furious Scots drawing up a 'National Covenant and Declaration of Faith' and sending it out for signature. It was carried like the Fiery Cross from end to end of the land, and thousands signed it, some in their own blood. Charles had to yield to their demand for a general assembly which met at Glasgow and proceeded to reject all his new rulings.

The King, furious in his turn and with no Parliament to vote the necessary funds, scraped together an army of sorts and marched north, but the Scots rushed to join in defence of their religion and their independence, under such officers as old Alexander Leslie, who had been Field-Marshal to Gustavus Adolphus of Sweden, the greatest soldier of his time. The King took one startled look at them, saw the hopelessness of taking on such a host, and asked for a truce.

Meanwhile Montrose, who had been one of the first to sign, was riding like a whirlwind about and about Scotland, gathering signatures and recruits, and when, a year later, the 'Bishop's War' broke out again, he led the army that he had gathered south, each man with a bunch of blue ribbons in his bonnet. They forded the Tweed in the dark, Montrose himself crossing first to encourage the men, then coming back to cross again with them. 'Ach, he will not drown; he was born to be hanged', they said proudly.

They swept south through Northumberland and into Durham, where they halted, offering an armistice on condition that an English Parliament was instantly summoned, and they were paid £25,000 a month for their expenses.

The King had no choice. He called the first Parliament in eleven years, who granted the Scots their expenses and then began proceedings against Archbishop Laud and the loyalist of the King's friends and advisers, Lord Strafford, who was finally beheaded in the following year.

Meanwhile Archibald Campbell—but now he was Argyll—had become virtual Master of all Scotland north of the Highland line. He had refused to openly join the Covenanters or the Committee of Estates that grew from them, saying that he might 'Help them the better in secret', but he was the power behind all Covenanting Scotland, a growing power, and he had begun to test the wind with small 'theoretical' remarks to his friends as to whether it might sometimes be right to depose the Lord's Annointed. Montrose, who fought the tyranny and the bad advisers, never the King. himself, grew more and more anxious as the deadly grip tightened on his beloved Scotland, at last wrote to warn the King of how things went, and begged him to come to the next Scottish Parliament.

But the correspondence was discovered, and when Charles came, Montrose was a prisoner in Edinburgh Castle on a trumped-up charge of treason, and despite all the efforts of the King himself to get him freed, there he remained until the royal visit was over, when the treason charge was dropped and he was set free again.

Argyll's determination that he should have no chance to speak with the King, and Argyll's power to prevent it, had shown him with even more appalling clearness, the threat brooding over Scotland. And the Scotland into which he was liberated, in which no book might now be published without rigid and bigoted censorship, the dead were refused burial if they had not signed the Covenant in life, and to pick gooseberries during sermon time or wish another man a Merry Christmas had become punishable offences, finished what his weeks in prison had begun. From then on, he was for the Covenant no more, for the Covenant had gone rotten. He was the King's man.

The King set up his standard at Nottingham on a blustery August day, and the wind blew it down again. The Civil War in England had begun and Montrose rode off to join the King.

'So the Earl of Montrose has changed his coat', said some.

'No', said others who knew him better. 'It is the cause that has changed; Montrose holds to the things he always held to.'

He had plans for bringing Scotland over to the Royalist side, but the King preferred to put his trust in his usual bad advisers and in the Duke of Argyll, and it was a weary while before, at last, Montrose seemed to get through to him and shake him into some kind of awareness of what he was talking about; longer still before he received his orders. . . .

He was to head North with a small force for the Border, where he was to be joined by Alisdair McDonald with a force of Antrim troops—McDonalds for the most part, who had been hounded westward to Ireland by the Campbells, and should therefore make good fighters against Argyll.

He rode out with his little band and two officers under him, Colonel Sibbald and Sir William Rollock, who was an old friend. They gained the Border, and managed to get word through to friends and families, but always the answer that came back was the same, 'If you had come a year ago—if only you had come a year ago. Now it is too late; Argyll's fist is clenched on the whole country!' The Antrim troops did not appear, and instead Montrose received a Marquisite from the King. He would rather have had pay for his troops. And then there was an urgent call from Prince Rupert, the King's nephew, to come to his aid in relieving besieged York. He flung his men south by forced marches, only to find that the Prince had attacked without waiting for him. Marston Moor had been fought and ended in defeat, losing most of the north to the royal cause.

He left nearly all his troops with Prince Rupert who was now desperately in need of men, and turned back towards the King's headquarters at Oxford, to report failure.

Then it seems he changed his mind. He sent on the baggage and the small bodyguard that were still left to him, to rejoin the King, and with Sibbald and Will Rollock headed again for the Border, but not in their own outward seeming. The two junior officers had become Covenanter troopers, while Montrose himself, his hair cut short and his hands stained with walnut juice and hacked ragged at the nails, was their groom.

They rode without let or hindrance through a countryside dusty with high summer and crawling with troops and fugitives, unrecognised by anyone until they came upon a drunken survivor from Marston Moor, singing in a ditch. Colonel Sibbald, not wanting to run into Royalist troops, stopped to ask him the whereabouts of his Company. He had lost them and didn't care, he was too happily drunk to care about anything, but his blurred gaze showed him what nobody else had seen, all the same, that the groom sitting slouched in the saddle of the third horse, was the Marquis of Montrose, and he wished him luck most heartily. He came very near to death in the next instant, but Montrose beat up his companion's sword, and gave the man a golden guinea for his silence, instead, and they rode on their way.

From that hour forward, for just one year, it seemed that the luck of the gods was with Montrose; that whatever the griefs and stresses of his private life, as the defender of Scotland's liberty he could not make a false move or lose a single battle.

They passed without trouble clean through Leslie's army and headed for Perth, where Montrose knew that he would find help and support from a cousin and bosom friend of his college days, 'Black Pate'. Their road passed not far from Kinnaird Castle, and he managed to get word to Magdelen. She came to meet him by night in a certain little spinney among the marshes where they had often met as children. They had an hour or so together, but before dawn he was on his way again.

Meanwhile, unknown to him, Alisdair McDonald had landed with a thousand men, called together as many as he could of the McDonalds of the west coast and, unable to get any word of Montrose, who seemed to have disappeared south of the Border soon after Marston Moor, had simply cast himself on his own luck and led them straight out into enemy country, to harry the Campbells, which seemed to any McDonald the obvious thing to do. He found that he had stirred up an army of Argyll's bigger by far than he could handle, and fell back to his ships to find that Argyll had had the forethought to burn them. He headed inland again to try to raise the country for the King, but too many of the clans had old grievances against the McDonalds, and he was near despair when at last he received word from Montrose to meet him at Blair. Alisdair marched off, took Blair Castle, and found himself penned in the midst of Athol clansmen who certainly hated Argyll and the Covenanters but hated the wild interlopers even more. Alisdair knew that it was only a matter of time before they attacked, but hung on, grimly and without hope.

And then out of nowhere, a slight young man in Highland dress with one follower at his shoulder, came walking over the brow of the heather hill, as though he had that moment sprung into being in a world that had been empty of him the moment before. And suddenly the word was racing through the little War Host, Montrose had come!

Beside Black Pate at his shoulder, his army, it seemed, consisted of two friends and three horses who would be here presently. No matter, the King's Lieutenant had come!

There was no time to be lost. Alisdair had roused most of the Highlands against him, and in the south the Covenanters were growing stronger every day. He must strike before they could join forces; he must have food for his men, horses, war supplies. They marched for Perth, where all these things were to be had, and midway there, met five hundred bowmen sent against Alisdair in the name of the Covenant. But their two leaders, Lord Kilpont and David Drummond were old St Andrew's friends of Montrose. They were out for the Irish McDonalds, it was unthinkable that they should fight Montrose, still sharing among them the glorious memory of the night they had tossed their arrows over St Salvator's Tower and shot the Provost's hat!

They joined forces with him and all marched on Perth together. They took the town, but to the disgust of Alisdair and most of his men, Montrose would allow no looting. The guns and gear of the dead outside the city walls, food and cloth for new coats and £50 demanded from the town, that was all. Any other man would have had a mutiny on his hands; even for Montrose it was a near thing, and most of the Athol Highlanders streamed away home with what little plunder they had been able to collect, according to their usual custom after a battle. In their place, Montrose gained one recruit. He had sent for his old tutor to bring the two eldest boys to him at Perth, for the Lord knew when he might get another sight of them; the eldest was fourteen, which counted near enough for a man in those days, and when eleven-year-old Jamie was sent home again, Johnnie rode on with his father. What their mother thought about it she never told to anyone.

Little bands of horse led by kinsmen and old friends came in to join them, and Montrose's crazy little army was back to something approaching its former strength again as they swept down on Aberdeen.

They halted before the gates, and Montrose sent in an envoy, and with him a drummer—the twelve-year-old bastard son of Kilpont—with word to surrender the town. The envoy came back alone and in a white rage. The young drummer had been shot as they were coming away. Montrose said little, but when Aberdeen also fell, there was no order against sack and pillage, and the streets ran red and half the town went up in flames for the wanton butchery of that one small drummer boy. Afterwards, Montrose must have felt sickened to his soul, for no other captured town was sacked during that wild year.

Alisdair turned westward to raise more troops, and Montrose, left with only five hundred men, knew that no more would come in to his standard now, for the tale of the sack of Aberdeen, magnificent Covenanter propaganda, was being widely and carefully spread. Less was heard of how Argyll was quietly and systematically carrying fire and sword among the homes of folk even vaguely suspected of Royalist sympathies.

Montrose filled in the waiting time by firing a few Covenanting roofs in return, and proceeded to lead Argyll and his great army a marsh-light dance that would at least keep them too busy to join Leslie in England. All autumn long it lasted, until on an evil day his scouts made a mistake and Montrose found himself defending a derelict castle run dry of ammunition, and in a trap with bog on three sides of him and the Covenanters outnumbering him five to one on the fourth.

But even now the luck that the drunken soldier had wished him did not altogether leave him. A charge of the wild Irish war bands captured them the powder they needed from the entrenchments of the enemy musketeers, and in the next few hours they ransacked the castle and melted down lead guttering, pewter pots and dishes and even a handsome supply of chamber pots, into the bullets they so sorely needed.

The job was barely done when word came in of five hundred Covenant cavalry advancing to the attack. Montrose's fifty horse were ready and waiting, and now they charged down to meet the Covenanters, each rider with a couple of musketeers clinging to his stirrups and leaping along beside him, until they dropped clear and poured in such a volley that the enemy cavalry, quite unprepared, turned and fled back to the main army, their arrival spread such chaos on all sides that the general fight that followed was over almost before it was begun. And Argyll, bitterly disheartened at his first attempt at open battle, pulled his troops back across the near-by river. Montrose brought off his whole force under cover of the early dark.

In November, Alisdair came back out of the west with a swarm of new recruits behind him. He and Montrose met again at Blair, and there was both feasting and councils of war. All that autumn they had kept the Covenanters from joining Leven in England; but now? Montrose was on fire to march for the Border, but the newly arrived Highlanders were less interested in King and Covenant than they were in settling old scores with the Campbells. And Montrose himself knew that it would be madness to take his troops south while the King's chief enemy was still powerful in Scotland, so he set his wild impatience aside and agreed. Campbells first.

Argyll was safe by now in winter quarters in his own Castle of Inverary on Loch Fyne, and none but Campbell scouts knew the passes through the hills into the heart of Campbell country. None, it seemed, save one man, who had been their captive and escaped: Angus MacAlain Duibb, a McDonald of Glencoe.

On Christmas Day Argyll and his family and household were in the kirk when the door crashed open and a wild-eyed shepherd burst in shouting that the McDonalds were upon them! The kirk emptied in a chaos of shouting men and shrieking women and the terrified howls of children. But of the fighting that followed, Argyll saw nothing, for he did not stop to share it with his people. He was away down Loch Fyne in a fishing-boat, with his wife and his shamed and furious young son who had had to be dragged aboard.

The victors ate fresh meat and drank strong ale, and rested for a few days, then marched for Inverness where Lord Seaforth held command. But towards the end of January, at the head of Loch Ness, they found themselves hemmed in again. Argyll with a hurriedly mustered army of three thousand men was hard on their heels and had got as far as Inverlochy only thirty miles to the south, so that they were caught between them and Lord Seaforth's troops, with another force of Covenanters under General Baillie inland of them and on their fourth side, the sea.

The first thing Montrose did on receiving the ugly news was to write out a bond binding all who signed it to fight to the death against the King's enemies. He signed it himself, then gave the pen to Johnnie, who signed close under him, and spent the rest of that day and part of the next in seeing that everyone of his force signed or made his mark if he could not write. It seems an odd time to be making such a bond, but its effect was exactly what Montrose intended. It calmed and steadied the wild Highlanders. And perhaps it had another purpose for himself also—to ensure that if he were killed, the world and the King's cause should know that he had not fought all these months in some mere Clan feud between McDonalds and Campbells, but for his King.

After that, it was time to get their own blow in first. They ate a good meal and marched for the Lochaber Mountains, knowing that save for a little barley-meal and water, they would not eat again until they ate in captured Inverlochy. They made it in thirty-six hours, scaling some of the wildest mountains in all Scotland in a frost to cut the feet from under them; and came at last over the skirts of Ben Nevis, to look down on Loch Linnhe and see the camp-fires of the Covenanters all about the Argyll Castle, and beside the landing stage a black galley lit at stern and stem. And even as they watched, the galley drew away from the shore and began to slip seaward on the dark water.

Their coming had been seen by the scouts, and though they were so few to his many, the Lord of the Campbells was once again in flight. It is not hard to imagine how, with every defeat, with every flight, his hatred must have grown and festered, for the man who had won the archery medal after him. . . .

When the sun rose, fifteen hundred of Argyll's clansmen lay dead, their green tartans soaked in red, along the shores of Loch Linnhe; and the power of Argyll lay in ruins.

Montrose marched to Elgin. No need for fighting now; men fairly fell over their own feet in their haste to join his standard and sign his bond. And among them, most welcome of all, an old friend and comrade, Colonel Nathaniel Gordon who had seemingly deserted to the Covenanters some while before, returned in triumph with two kinsmen, Lord George Gordon and his younger brother, Lewis, rescued from captivity, and two hundred clansmen at his back to show for the adventure. Now the whole army moved into the Bog of Gite and made headquarters at Gordon Castle. And there, Johnnie, who had made the great Lochaber Mountain march with them, finally foundered, and was put to bed to recover. Only he did not recover. What had seemed only exhaustion became fever, and he had no strength left to fight it.

Johnnie died in his father's arms, and was buried in the near-by kirkyard, in the midst of a clan that was not his own, with half the chieftains of Scotland to see him to his grave, and half the pipers of Scotland to play their laments over him.

Montrose turned from the kirkyard to the next stage of the campaign that must still go on. Once again he was short of supplies and as usual after victory, his men were melting away. If he could have paid them regularly so that they had had money to send home, he could and would have treated them as deserters, but the King, who had promised him pay money had never sent it, and he could not hunt down and shoot men whose families would starve if they did not go home to help them keep the crofts going. He was down to about six hundred men, less than a quarter of the number he had had a month ago; something must be done quickly, very quickly indeed.

He sent the weaker part of his army on to Brechin with the baggage while with the rest he marched on Dundee, the strongest Covenanting town in Angus.

Arriving before the gates, he summoned the town to surrender and getting no reply, stormed the walls and turned the captured guns on the town. Dundee thought better of its refusal to yield and he entered the town to meet the citizens and receive their surrender, while his men swarmed through the shops and warehouses after food and cloth and drink. They had gone hungry for many days in the cold spring weather, they had marched all night without a halt, and now they seized on the beer and wine and drink till, too dog-weary to get drunk in the ordinary sense, many of them dropped in the streets and slept where they lay.

And as they lay there, a scout came galloping with news that Baillie and three thousand Covenanters were within a mile of the west gate.

Montrose was on the walls when the word came, and as he hurried back into the town, his officers joined him, running from all quarters. Alisdair was for making a stand at the west port and pulling as many of the enemy down to hell with them as they could. Some of his lowland comrades shouted to Montrose to save himself and gather a new army. Young Lewis Gordon was for firing the town and burning it over their own heads as well as the enemy's. But Montrose had other ideas, and he sent the officers about him running, each with the same orders, to gather their own men and somehow, anyhow, get them out through the east port; orders which seemed impossible to carry out, with all the soldiers dead-weary and half of them dead drunk. But somehow the thing was done. His few cavalry officers turned sheep dog, routing men out from the four streets and the market square, and driving them towards the east port. Word that the Covenanters were upon them ran like heath-fire through the town, rousing those still able to hear and understand, so that they stumbled to their feet and kicked up the rest; and somehow, shouting, cursing, the whole lot were rounded up and driven at sword-point through the east port. As Montrose with the tiny rearguard rode out under the gate arch, the Covenanters were clattering in through the west port.

Somehow their officers got them sorted out, the most drunken and most weary in front, where they could be kept going 'at push of pike', the cavalry and the more sober of the musketeers in the rear, against the time when the enemy must discover them gone and come after them. The attack came when they had gone only a few miles northward, struggling through the heavy spring rain that had begun to fall. Somehow they drove it off, and pushed on again. A party of enemy cavalry had got ahead of them, but by a swing went into the hills before turning north again, Montrose outflanked them, and somehow dragged and drove his scarecrow company on—and on. Once more they beat off an attack, and then at last they were in the familiar hills that had been their shelter and their stronghold for so long. They were met by the troops that Montrose had sent on to Brechin with the baggage train. The rain had stopped; here among the bogs and the steep rocky hillsides they were safe from the heavily armed and mounted Covenanters. And they dropped into the heather more drunk with exhaustion than ever they had been with beer, to finish the sleep that they had begun in the streets of Dundee a day and a night ago.

The fame of that march rang through Scotland more loudly than the tale of any of Montrose's victories. For the present, at least, there were no more desertions.

Montrose's Army was like an army of the mist. The size and shape of it changed from day to day, and from day to day no man knew its position or its next purpose. In April, the King's Lieutenant found breathing space to go home to Magdelen for a few days. It was her father's house he went to, for it had seemed best, in these troubled times, that he should leave her there, but ever since their marriage, home to him, had been wherever Magdelen was, and going back to her had been going home. She did not know of his coming until his horse was trampling at the outer gates, and she ran out just in time to meet him with a stirrup cup as he dismounted in the courtyard, remembering perhaps how when he was a boy he had always insisted on his horse having one, too. He had his few days with her, a few days to try to comfort her for Johnnie's death and to draw comfort from her in his turn. Then there was another stirrup cup and he rode away again, about the King's business. That was the last time, save once, that he saw Magdelen alive.

In early May he fought another great battle at Aldearn, when magnificent charge led by Lord George, the elder of the Gordon brothers, turned the day, and they drove the beaten enemy clear off the field.

In July, close to the village of Alford they did it again, and all but captured Argyll himself into the bargain. But there was small joy in that victory, for in the moment of it, George Gordon was shot by a stray bullet, and as the grieving clansmen gathered about the body of their young chief, Montrose knew not only that the best hope of his cause was gone, but that though they had been friends only a few months, he had lost the boy he loved best in the world after Johnnie.

Another victory followed in August, at Kilsyth, where the Highlanders, for the sake of speed and freedom in the shimmering heat, flung off their plaids and charged uphill clad only in their saffron shirts, their claymores flashing in the late summer sun, their heads ducked behind their round bucklers. That was a very great battle, with five thousand men following Montrose's standard and seven thousand under that of the Covenant. And when it was over, there was no Covenanting Army left north of the Border, and Montrose was recognised far and wide as the King's representative, the Master of Scotland.

But the leaders had escaped, and the year had come full circle since a drunken soldier in a ditch had wished him good luck.

It did not show at first. Chiefs who had never thought of joining him before came crowding in now, among them the Chief of the Douglas Clan. He admitted freely when he arrived, that the Douglas chieftains were not now of the same mettle as their ancestor who had set out to take The Bruce's heart to the Holy Land, but he trusted that Montrose would find his coming better late than never. He was quite unashamed, in fact cynically amused at his own shortcomings, and it was that perhaps that made Montrose's heart warm to him, for he always liked a man who could laugh at himself.

On a golden September day Sir Robert Spottiswood, the King's Secretary of State for Scotland, arrived in the camp with a letter from the King appointing James Graham, 1st Marquis of Montrose, his Lieutenant Governor of Scotland. This meant that he now had power to summon Parliament, and he immediately summoned one, to meet in Glasgow in October.

He had kept the promise he had made to the King, to raise Scotland for him, though the King had not kept his to send pay for his soldiers . . . to come himself. . . . Now the King bade him march south, joining forces on the way with the Border Earls. Montrose wrote to the King triumphantly that he hoped in a few days to cross the Tweed with at least twenty thousand men to His Majesty's aid, and inquired where they should meet, since Spottiswood had been unable to tell him.

The King was being entertained at Raglan by the Marquis of Worcester, and he returned to Montrose's letter a charming and extremely non-committal answer. England was as good as lost to him now and the Scots his only hope, yet he lingered day after pleasant day at Raglan, and while he lingered, David Leslie, a greater kinsman of Old Alexander Leslie, who was besieging Hereford, received urgent word from Argyll of the defeat of Kilsyth and Montrose's advance towards the Border, and raising the siege, marched north with the main part of his army to join Argyll at Newcastle.

If the King had been about his business he could have intercepted them, but he was still hunting at Raglan in the delightful
142

autumn weather. The road was clear, and David Leslie passed through.

By that time, Alisdair, the part of the fighting that interested him being over, had taken his Irish and his Highlanders and disappeared back to the west, and two days later, Lewis Gordon took his men—the greater part of the cavalry—and flung off also, because Montrose had not, to his mind, given him the love and honour that he had given to George. Many of Montrose's friends urged him to take to the hills again, and set about raising the Clans once more. But that would take time, and the time was running out, with David Leslie on the march north. No, he must march south with what men he still had—Douglas had gone to beat up recruits in his own lowlands—and trust that when they were joined by the Border Lords, Hume and Roxborough, their numbers might be somewhere not far short of the twenty thousand, after all.

They rode into Kelso on September 8th, but there was no sign of Hume or Roxborough who should have met them there. Montrose waited a day and night that he could ill afford. And then the news came. Misliking the idea of joining such a shrunken army, they had surrendered to Leslie as the easiest way out of an awkward situation.

Nothing for it, then, but to turn back to the hills after all, and begin again from the beginning. But first he must write to Charles, a letter that would be bitter hard in the writing, to tell him that in the very hour of its success, the enterprise had collapsed after all. He was going to fail his King. It was the direct result of the King having failed *him*, but that made no difference to James Graham, Marquis of Montrose.

They reached Selkirk on the evening of September 12th. He ordered a general muster for next daybreak, for the start of their march back into the hills. He left his men encamped on level ground below the town—a meadow called Philiphaugh where the streams of Yarrow and Ettric met—sent out mounted patrols who reported the country clear for many miles (how they came to do so remains a mystery; it is possible that their local guides were in the pay of Argyll), but for the first time, left the ordering of the scouts and sentries to his officers. The letter was gnawing at him like a rat; dead-weary as he was, he must get it written before he slept. He went back into Selkirk, to the house in the west port where he had made his headquarters, had a council of war with one or two of his cavalry leaders, and settled down to the bitter task.

In the early hours of the morning he finished it, and lay down to snatch an hour or two of sleep. And while he slept a mist crept over the countryside. . . .

He was up again at first light and snatching a few hasty mouthfuls of bannock, when his scout master burst into the room shouting that the enemy were upon them, thousands strong and all cavalry.

In the camp, when he came down into it at the flying gallop, he found red chaos. The men had been cooking their breakfast when the Covenanters charged them out of the concealing mist. The Irish five hundred were fighting like heroes. But Douglas's new Lowland levies were running like rabbits without firing a shot. Of all the Lowland troops and nobles, Douglas, the unashamed late-comer was the only one who stayed. Maybe not such a sorry descendant of that other Douglas, after all. Montrose and he got together about a hundred Horse, and made such a valiant charge that for the moment the whole black cloud of Covenant cavalry was checked. But Leslie had divided his army in two, and now there came a crack and rattle of musketry from the rear. The firing was almost blind in the mist, but in the packed chaos of the camp men were falling in all directions. They were surrounded and hemmed in, and though the little knot of Royalist cavalry drove their charge narrow and deep into the enemy ranks, the Covenanters crashed in again and again, wave after wave out of the mist like the waves of a pounding sea.

Only a hundred of the Irish were left now, the little valiant cavalry band were down by half, as they fell back on Philiphaugh farm to sell their lives as dearly as they could. And Leslie, seeing no point in losing more of his own men, when the end was sure anyway, made a promise of quarter to any man who would surrender.

With the promise of quarter, there was no point in going on dying. The Irish flung down their arms. Montrose was still fighting; men said after that he looked gay as a bridegroom. Douglas thrust his own horse up beside him, urging him to try at least to cut his way through and escape—get away and gather another army for the King. But Montrose saw at that moment little point in going on gathering armies for the King. Better to die now and be done with it. But other voices were added to the Douglas's, and now about thirty of his friends had gathered about him, all of his army who yet lived and had not flung down their weapons in surrender.

They charged knee to knee; they broke through and out-

distanced their pursuers, and found at last the road to the hills clear before them.

So the Covenant was in full power again, and the promise of mercy to those who had surrendered was overruled by command of the Kirk ministers. The officers had the distinction of being taken to Edinburgh and hanged from the castle wall without trial, while the unarmed clansmen simply had the troopers let loose on them and were butchered where they stood and as they ran.

'The work goes on bonnily,' said one minister of God.

Montrose in the hills got word of the executions, and amid these bloody. tidings, word also from his father-in-law that Magdelen was dying.

He rode down from the hills and headed eastward for Kinnaird, going home to her, for the last time. Between himself and Magdelen the country was swarming with dragoons, but he must see her again, alive or dead. He got through the dragoons and rode into the courtyard of Kinnaird Castle, and her father came down to meet him. She was still alive, but had been unconscious for many hours, and was already drifting out on the dark waters. It was certain that she would not open her eyes again.

He went up to their room and stood beside the great bed where he had carried her as a bride, feeling a stone in his breast where his living heart should have been. She had waited for him so often and so long, but this time she had not been able to wait long enough, and would never know that he had come back this last time of all. But as though some awareness of him reached her wherever she was drifting, and called her back, she did open her eyes once more, and saw him standing there, and gave him the shadow of a smile.

And then she was gone.

The Great Year was well and truly over, and hardly had he begun the thankless task of raising troops yet again, than he received word from Charles that he had decided to give himself up to his enemies, and the best way in which Montrose could now save the cause was by dismissing the rest of his soldiers and taking himself overseas.

So Montrose went abroad, to wander from Court to Court through Europe trying to raise troops for the King, and the King gave himself up to the Covenanters on promise of safeguard, to be promptly handed over to Cromwell by the man he had not long since raised from Earl to Marquis of Argyll.

He landed in Scotland again just a year after Charles's execution, to raise the Clans for Charles II. But the old luck had now quite deserted him; his fistful of fighting men were surprised and routed, and Montrose, escaping into country that was strange to him, went for shelter to the Lord of Assynt, whom he believed to be a friend—and was betrayed and carried captive to Edinburgh.

Argyll hurried on the execution without a trial, for the thing must be done quickly before the storm of protest rising all over Europe should make it impossible to be done at all.

On a stormy day in early summer the Marquis of Montrose, wounded, starving and with his hands bound behind him, was drawn in the hangman's cart through the streets of Edinburgh to the waiting gallows in the Grass-Market. People had been brought there, even paid, to throw stones and filth at him as the cart rattled by. A few women, the widows of men his Highlanders had killed, threw their stones, and screamed their curses. For the rest, there was not a sound, not a movement in the vast crowd that lined the cannongate save where here and there a man or woman fell on their knees to pray. But Montrose in the death cart seemed withdrawn beyond the reach of stones and dead cats and prayers alike. Afterwards, men said of him that he looked very peaceful, almost happy, like a man who has come to the end of a long wild road and sees the light in his home window clear before him. . . .

When all was over they hacked up his body as butchers hack up the carcass of a sheep, and sent the quarters to the chief towns of Scotland. But friends risked their lives to steal away his heart, and had it enclosed in a small steel case—it is surprising how small the heart is when out of the body, even such a heart as Montrose's—made from the blade of his sword. And in course of time it came to young Jamie in exile in Holland.

And so—there is an end of Heroes, and the Hero-light dims out. Or maybe not. Maybe even in this modern world and on into the future, the old breed will still break through from time to time, and some man will stride out from among the rest, with that strange quality of being larger than life, and enlarging the lives of those who come within his orbit. And the legends, in one form or another, will gather again.

Index